REPRINTS OF ECONOMIC CLASSICS

A FULL AND DETAILED CATALOGUE OF BOOKS

WHICH BELONGED TO

ADAM SMITH

NOW IN THE POSSESSION OF THE FACULTY OF ECONOMICS, UNIVERSITY OF TOKYO

A full and detailed Catalogue of Books

which belonged to

Adam Smith

Now in the possession of the Faculty
of Economics, University of Tokyo
With Notes and Explanations

by

TADAO YANAIHARA *Dr. Econ.*,

Professor of the Faculty of Economics,
University of Tokyo

THE ADAM SMITH LIBRARY

REPRINTS OF ECONOMIC CLASSICS

AUGUSTUS M. KELLEY · PUBLISHERS
NEW YORK · 1966

FIRST PUBLISHED 1951

LIBRARY OF CONGRESS CATALOGUE CARD NUMBER

66 - 15562

PRINTED IN THE UNITED STATES OF AMERICA
by SENTRY PRESS, NEW YORK, N. Y. 10019

INTRODUCTION

It is fortunate for the Faculty of Economics, University of Tokyo, to possess 141 books or entries (308 volumes) which belonged to the library of Adam Smith. They consist of 62 books or entries (98 volumes) in English, 34 books or entries (43 volumes) in Latin, 28 books or entries (92 volumes) in French, 15 books (73 volumes) in Italian, and 2 books (2 volumes) in German. The subjects of these books cover the wide range of philosophy, literature and poetry, politics, history and biography, geography and topography of various countries, travels, natural history, religion, arts, art of war, language, mathematics, etc., but no book on economics save the chief work of Adam Smith himself and its German translation.

These books were purchased by the late Professor Inazo Nitobé, and donated by him to our Faculty on the occasion of its foundation as a separate faculty in the University. One day while staying in London in 1920, he happened to notice in a catalogue of Messrs. Dulau & Co. Ltd., that these books were on sale. He hurried to the book-seller, and was just in time, to his great joy, to contract for these books for our Faculty. At his direction Messrs. Dulau & Co. Ltd. packed them in six boxes, and sent them to us with the following letter of certification.

"At the death of Adam Smith, his library went by will to David Douglas, afterwards Lord Reston. On Lord Reston's death the library was divided between his two daughters, Mrs. Cunningham and Mrs. Bannerman. Mrs. Cunningham gave her portion to her son Professor Cunningham, Queen's College, Belfast. After the death of Professor Cunningham the library was sold in 1918 to Messrs. Dulau & Co. Ltd.,

London from whom Dr. I. Nitobe purchased it in July 1920.

Dulau & Co. Ltd.

Fw. Chaundy, Director."

Since the arrival of the books in Tokyo, they have survived two great catastrophies. One was the earthquake and fire of 1923, which had burned down the Library of our Faculty too. But by the brave efforts of certain servants of the Faculty, Adam Smith's library was rescued from the raging fire.

The other catastrophe came with the late war. By the successive bombings, many buildings and homes of Tokyo were burned to ashes. Before the bombings of Tokyo became severe, the authorities of our Faculty had removed some important books to a safer place in the country. As a matter of fact, the buildings of the University of Tokyo were spared from direct attack, nor had they become victims of the fire which devoured their neighbourhood. Anyhow, Adam Smith's library has survived the War, and is still in our safe custody, without even one volume missing. The bindings of some books have suffered damage, owing to careless treatment and frequent removals at those two critical occasions, but this may be regarded as a minor calamity compared with a possible loss of the books themselves.

At the request of Dr. James Bonar, the late Professor Eijiro Kawai of our Faculty compiled a list of our Adam Smith Library, and supplied him with a copy of it. Dr. Bonar has acknowledged the help received, and says that thus about twenty books not before catalogued have been newly added to the second edition of his "A Catalogue of the Library of Adam Smith," 1932. (cf. his Introduction pp. xvii-xviii, and Appendix VI. p. 214.) Only we are sorry to say that Kawai's list was incomplete and unsatisfactory in many points, and the results of its incompleteness are evident in Bonar's Catalogue.

This year (1949) we have celebrated the thirtieth anniversary of the foundation of the Faculty of Economics, University of Tokyo, and in commemoration of the occasion I have undertaken to edit a full and detailed catalogue of our Adam Smith Library. The Japan Science Council has furnished financial aid for this work; and by the help of many friends and colleagues, among whom Mr. Mitsuna Nagaminé and Mr. Fukumatsu Miwa should be specially mentioned for their valuable services, I was enabled to finish it.

As to the form of entry, we have consulted with the catalogues of the Library of Congress and of the British Museum. Concerning the very interesting way in which Adam Smith used his library to build up his thoughts, or to get materials for his study; how he quoted or referred to those authorities in his own books; we owe much to Dr. Bonar's catalogue.

I have carefully compared my investigations with Bonar's catalogue. At the right hand of each entry, I have indicated the page of Bonar's catalogue, 2nd ed., where the same book is entered. Wherever there is any difference between Bonar's catalogue and my own, I have so indicated it. At least as far as the books in our possession are concerned, my entry may be considered correct. Where Bonar's entry coincides with mine, I have indicated only his page.

Appendix I contains a list of two books, which were sent to us by Messrs. Dulau & Co. Ltd., together with other books. But in respect to their dates of publication, both following the death of Adam Smith (1790), it is evidently proper to exclude them from a catalogue of books which "belonged to Adam Smith." They might have been added to the library of Adam Smith after his death.

In Appendix II, I have shown the full contents of "A Catalogue of Books belonging to Adam Smith, Esqr. 1781." It is a handwriting manuscript, and I have had some difficulties in deciphering the letters. We have done our best, but still I am afraid of possible mistakes. I have tried to reproduce the spellings of words as they are in the manuscript. In the original there are no marks of accentuation at all. The apostrophes are irregular, but I have left them all as they stand in the manuscript.

In Prof. Kawai's list, which he supplied to Dr. Bonar, this catalogue was dated erroneously as 1761. This had caused quite a sensation among British scholars, because if the date were really 1761, this catalogue "made either for or by Adam Smith himself, would show what was in his library at that date, when he was Professor at Glasgow and had published the *Moral Sentiments,* but no book in economics." (Bonar, Catalogue of Adam Smith's Library. 2nd ed. 1932. p. 214.) Dr. Bonar wished that "our Japanese friends will satisfy our curiosity in this matter." (ibid.) Prof. Scott noticed this point, and asked Prof. Kawai to supply him with a photographic copy of the original manuscript. Eventually he discovered that the date written is 1781, instead of 1761, and the question was settled. (cf. Prof. Scott, Adam Smith as Student and Professor, 1937. pp. 172, 390.)

As "the catalogue in Rae, p. 52, dated 1792, possibly a lawyer's inventory, has not been found," (Bonar, Catalogue, 2nd ed. p. 174.) this catalogue of 1781 seems to be the only one which Adam Smith drew up himself.

The catalogue of 1781 contains about 1120 books or entries (2300 volumes). I have compared this catalogue with Bonar's (2nd ed.), and have marked his entries, as far as I could, with the page of entry in it. Readers will discover that many books listed in the catalogue of 1781 have not been catalogued by Bonar.

I am one of those who hold the opinion that the thoughts and works of Adam Smith are still worth studying. Without knowing the thoughts of the 18th century, we are unable to grasp the democracy of the 20th century. I hope this cataloguing of books which belonged once to the great economist of Scotland may serve not only to "satisfy curiosity", but to stimulate among us fresh efforts to study his thoughts, as well as those of the 18th century in general.

I cannot conclude my introduction without expressing my hearty thanks and gratitude to all those who helped and assisted me willingly in this troublesome work of cataloguing, as well as for the generous co-operation of Messrs. Iwanami Shoten, who bore the expense of publishing. They offered to do this as their contribution to the celebration of the thirtieth anniversary of our Faculty.

TADAO YANAIHARA

Dean of the Faculty of Economics,
University of Tokyo.

August 27th, 1949

CONTENTS

Adam Smith's Library at the Tokyo University.
The bookplate of Adam Smith.
First page of the Catalogue of Adam Smith's Library, 1781.
P. 10 of the Catalogue of Adam Smith's Library, 1781.
The title-page of the German Translation of "The Wealth of Nations," Vol. I, 1776.
The engraved added title-page of Thomas Hobbes' Leviathan.

ERRATA.

CATALOGUE

1. **Alembert, Jean Le Rond d', 1717-1783.**

Histoire des membres de l'Académie françoise, morts depuis 1700 jusqu'en 1771, pour servir de suite aux Éloges imprimés et lus dans les séances publiques de cette compagnie. Par M. d'Alembert, Secrétaire perpétuel de l'Académie Françoise, et Membre des Académies des Sciences de France, d'Angleterre, de Prusse, de Russie, de Suede, de Portugal, de Bologne, de Turin, de Naples, de Cassel, de Boston et de Norwege. A Paris, Chez Moutard, 1779-87.

6 v. 17 cm.

Head and tail pieces.

Book plate: Adam Smith.

Vol. 1 has title-page: Éloges lus dans les séances publiques de l'Académie françoise, par M. d'Alembert... Paris, Chez Panckoucke, Moutard, 1779.

Vols. 2-6, published by Moutard, 1785-87.

On the references by Adam Smith to French Encyclopedists, see Bonar, pp. 3-5.

2. **[Altmann, Johann Georg] 1695-1758.**

L'Etat et les délices de la Suisse, ou Description helvétique historique et géographique. Nouvelle édition, corrigée & considérablement augmentée, par plusieurs auteurs celebres. Enrichis de figures en tailles douces & de cartes géographiques. A Basle, Chez E. Tourneisen, 1764.

Bonar, p. 3.

Entry:
Éloges lus dans les Séances publiques de l'Académie Françoise.
Date: 1779.

Bonar, p. 186.

Heading:
Tourneisen.

3

4 v. fold. plates (incl. map) 16½ cm.

Title vignette, in red and black.
Vol. 1 title-page wanted.
Published anonymously.

Book plate: Adam Smith.

3. **Amelot de La Houssaye, Abraham Nicolas,**
    1634-1706.

Histoire du gouvernement de Venise, par le sieur
Amelot de la Houssaie. Derniere edition, revûe, cor-
rigée & augmentée, avec figures. A Amsterdam, Chez
D. Mortier, 1714.

3 v. front., fold. map, fold. plates 16½ cm.

Title vignette, in red and black.
Title of vol. 3 reads: Histoire du gouvernement de
Venise, ou L'histoire des Uscoques...

Vol. 1 and 2 paged continuously.

"Examen de la liberte originaire de Venise, tr. de
l'italien. Avec une Harangue de Loüis Hélian, tr. du
latin..." (with special title-page): vol. 2, pp. 633-823.

Vol. 3 is a translation of the "Storia degli Uscochi"
by Minuccio Minucci, and the supplement to this work
by Paolo Sarpi.

Book plate: Adam Smith.

Minucci, Minuccio, abp. of Zara, 1551-1604.
Sarpi, Paolo, 1552-1623.

4. **Anderson, James,** 1662-1728.

Selectus diplomatum & numismatum Scotiæ thesaurus, in duas partes distributus: prior syllogen com-
plectitur verterum diplomatum sive chartarum regum
& procerum Scotiæ, una cum eorum sigillis, a Dun-
cano II. ad Jacobum I. id est ab anno 1094 ad 1412.
Adjuncta sunt reliquorum Scotiæ & Magnæ Britanniæ regum sigilla, à prædicto Jacobo I. ad nuperam duo-
rum regnorum in unum, anno 1707, coalitionem; item

characteres & abbreviaturæ in antiquis codicibus mss. instrumentisque usitatæ. Posterior continet numismata... singulorum Scotiæ regum, ab Alexandro I. ad supradictam regnorum coalitionem... subnexis... regum symbolis heroicis... Adjectis singulorum diplomatum, recentiore scripturæ formâ, æri... incisis exemplis. Ex mandato parliamenti scotici collegit, digessit & tantum non perficienda curavit... Jacobus Andersonus... Quæ operi consummando deerant supplevit, & præfatione, tabularum explicatione, aliisque appendicibus... auxit & locupletavit Thomas Ruddimannus, A. M. Suppeditante sumptus... Thomas Patersono... Edinburgi, Apud T. & W. Ruddimannos, 1739.

viii, 126 p. clxx pl. (including frontispiece, facsims.) 47 cm.

Title in red and black.

Ms. on title-page: William Smith.

Ms. on fly-leaf: Cunningham (?)

Book plate: Adam Smith.

Ruddiman, Thomas, 1674-1757, ed.

Preface by Ruddiman quoted in W. of N. three times. (Cannan's ed. i. p. 184, 212, 280.) see Bonar, p. 6.

5. **Antonini, Annibale,** 1702-1755.

Dictionaire italien, latin, et frahçois; contenant non seulement un abregé du dictionaire de la Crusca, mais encore tout ce qu'il y a de plus remarquable dans les meilleurs Lexicographes, Etymologistes, & Glossaires, qui ont paru en differentes Langues. Par M. l'abbé Antonini. Paris, Chez J. Vincent, 1735-43.

2 v. front. 26 cm.

Title in red and black, title vignette.

Book plate: Adam Smith.

Title of vol. 2 reads: Dictionaire françois, latin, et italien... seconde partie. Paris, Chez Prault, 1743.

Bonar, p. 7.

Date: 1735

6. **Anville, Jean Baptiste Bourguignon d',** 1697-1782.   Bonar, p. 8.

Analyse géographique de l'Italie, dédiée à mon-
seigneur le duc d'Orleans, premier prince du Sang.
Par le sieur d'Anville... A Paris, Chez la Veuve
Estienne & fils, 1744.

10 p. l., 288, [2] p. illus., 2 fold. maps. 26 cm.

Head and tail pieces.

Book plate: Adam Smith.

7. —— *ditto* ——   Bonar, p. 8.

Antiquité géographique de l'Inde, et de plusieurs
autres contrées de la Haute Asie. Par M. d'Anville...
A Paris, de l'Imprimerie royale, 1775.

xii, 238, 11 p. 3 fold. maps. (incl. front.) 26 cm.

Book plate: Adam Smith.

8. **Ariosto, Lodovico,** 1474-1533.   Bonar, p. 10.

Orlando furioso di Ludovico Ariosto. In Parigi,
appresso Prault, 1746.

4 v. front. 14½ cm.

Engraved title-page.

Book plate: Adam Smith.

*Ariosto is referred to by Adam Smith in Essays,
ed. 1795: Italian Verses, p. 189. See Bonar, p. 10.*

9. **Barrington, Daines,** 1727-1800.   Bonar, p. 18.
    Date: 1787

Miscellanies, by the honourable Daines Barrington... London, printed by J. Nichols, sold by B. White
[etc.] 1781.

6 p. l., 557, [1] p. 2 ports., fold. map, 5 geneal.
tables (1 fold.) chart. 27½×21½ cm.

Title vignette.

Book plate: Adam Smith.

Contents:

Tracts on the possibility of reaching the North Pole.

Miscellaneous essays.

Whether the turkey was known before the discovery of America.

On the rein-deer.

On the bat, or rere-mouse.

On the sudden decay of several trees in St. James's Park.

On the periodical appearing and disappearing of certain birds at different times of the year.

On the torpidity of the swallow tribe when they disappear.

On the prevailing notions with regard to the cuckow.

On the Linnaean system.

Other articles of contents.

Particulars of an agreement between the King of Spain and the Royal Society, for exchange of natural curiosities.

Account of {
Mozart,... musician.
Mr. Charles Wesley.
Master Samuel Wesley.
little Crotch.
the Earl of Mornington.
}

Of the deluge in the time of Noah.

History of the Gwedir family.

Letter, intended for Dodsley's museum, on the English and French writers.

Dialogue on the ancient tragedies, written at Oxford in 1746.

Ohthere's voyage, and the geography of the Ninth Century illustrated.

Journal of a Spanish voyage in 1775, to explore the western coast of N. America.

10. **Bell, John,** 1691-1780.

Travels from St. Petersburg in Russia, to diverse parts of Asia... By John Bell... Glasgow, printed for the author by R. and A. Foulis, 1763.

2 v. front. (fold. map) 24½×19 cm.

Book plate: Adam Smith.

Among the subscribers: Adam Smith, L.L.D. professor of Moral Philosophy in the University of Glasgow.

Vol. 1.   A journey from St. Petersburg in Russia, to Ispahan in Persia, with an embassy from His Imperial Majesty, Peter the First, to the Sophy of Persia, Shach Hussein, 1715, 1716, 1717, and 1718.

A journey from St. Petersburg in Russia, to Pekin in China, with an embassy from His Imperial Majesty, Peter the First, to Kamhi, Emperor of China, through Siberia, 1719-21, with map of route.

Vol. 2.   The continuation of the journey between Mosco and Pekin.

Journal of the Residence of Mr. de Lange, Agent of His Imperial Majesty of all the Russians, Peter the First, at the Court of Pekin, during the years 1721 and 1722. Translated from the French, printed at Leyden by Abraham Kallewier, 1726.

A succinct relation of my journey to Derbent in Persia, with the Army of Russia commanded by His Imperial Majesty Peter the First, 1722.

An Account of my journey from St. Petersburg to Constantinople, 1737-38, undertaken at the instances of Count Osterman, Chancellor of Russia, and of Mr. Rondeau, Minister from Great Britain at the court of St. Petersburg.

W. of N. (Cannan's ed.) ii. p. 178, note: "Your beggarly commerce!" said the mandarins of Pekin, as reported by "Mr. De Lange in Bell's Travels, ii. p. 259, 276, 293." See Bonar, p. 22.

The texts of the Journal of de Lange referred to by Adam Smith run as follows:—

"The Allegamba had, at the same time, added these words, 'The merchants come here to enrich themselves, not our people, which is easy to be seen, because they pretend themselves to fix the price of their own goods, that they may sell them the dearer... we will not embarrass ourselves hereafter with the merchants of Russia'." p. 258. (Adam Smith put it down as 259, incorrectly.)

"These foreigners come here with their commerce, to encumber us every moment with a thousand petty affairs, pretending that they ought to be favoured, on all occasions, no more nor less than if they laid an obligation on us." p. 276.

"That they expected to have been freed from their importuning the council about *their beggarly commerce,* after they had been told so often, that the council would not embarrass themselves any more about affairs that were only beneficial to the Russians; and that, of course, they had only to return by the way they came." p. 293.

11. **Bellori, Giovanni Pietro,** 1615?-1696.

Le vite de' pittori, scvltori et architetti moderni, scritte da Gio: Pietro Bellori, parte prima all'illvstriss. et eccellentiss. Signore Gio: Battista Colbert... In Roma, Per il succeso. al Mascardi, 1672.

6 p.l., 3-462 (i.e. 460) p. incl. engr. plates, engr. ports. engr. front. 23½ cm.

Engraved initials and head-pieces.

Nos. 137-140 wanting in paging; no. 391 and 392 duplicated.

No more published.

Book plate: Adam Smith, and (?)

Ms. tables of "The third three months assesment of the 36 granted for a Royall aide to his matir" on front and end fly-leaves.

12. **Benjamin ben Jonah,** *of Tudela*, 12th cent.

Itinerarium Benjaminis, latine redditum operâ Const. l'Empereur. Lugd. Batavorum, ex officinâ Elzeviriana, 1633.

36 p.l., 233, [7]p. 9×4½ cm.

Printer's device on title-page.

Bonar, p. 23.
Date : 1632.

13. **Boiardo, Matteo Maria,** *conte di Scandiano,* 1440 or 41-1494.

Orlando innamorato del S. Matteo Maria Boiardo, conte di Scandiano. Insieme co i tre libri di M. Nicolo degli Agostini, già riformati per M. Lodouico Domenichi. Nuouamente ristampato, e ricorretto, conuuoui argomenti allegorie, & bellissime figure ad ogni canto. In Venetia, appresso Domenico Imberti, 1611.

4 p.l., 450 numbered 1. illus. 20½ cm.

Printer's device on title-page.
Initials, head and tail pieces.

Book plate: Adam Smith.

Ms. on title-page. Franc: Massuc:.

Bonar, p. 32.

14. —— *ditto* ——

Orlando innamorato di Matteo M. Bojardo, rifatto da Francesco Berni. Parigi, appresso Molini, 1768.

4 v. front. (port.) 14½ cm.

Title vignette.

Bonar, p. 26.
Heading: Berni.

Book plate: Adam Smith.

Berni, Francesco, 1497 or 8-1535.

15. Boissy, Louis de, 1694-1758.

Œuvres de Monsieur de Boissy, contenant son théâtre françois et italien. Nouvelle édition, revuë, corrigée, & augmentée de plusieurs piéces nouvelles... A Amsterdam & Berlin, Chez J. Neaulme, 1768.

Vol. 5 only. 17½ cm.

Head pieces, initials.

Book plate: Adam Smith.

Bonar, p. 31.

No. of vols.:
Tome 15ème.

16. [Boxhorn, Marcus Zuerius] *d.* 1653.

Respublica Moscoviæ et urbes. Accedunt quædam latinè nunquam antehac edita. Lugduni Batavorum, ex efficina Ioannis Maire, 1630.

8 p.l., 287, [1] 192, [5] p. 11½×5½ cm.

Engraved title-page.

Dedication signed: Marcus Boxhorn-Zverius.

Paged separately "Pars chorographica", "Pars politica" and "Pars historica".

Bound with "Russia seu Moscovia itemque Tartaria... 1630".

Bonar,
No entry.

17. Buffon, Georges Louis Leclerc, comte de, 1707-1788.

Histoire naturelle générale et particulière, avec la description du Cabinet du roy... A La Haye, Chez P. de Hondt; Amsterdam, J. H. Schneider, 1750-81.

21 v. (i.e. tome 1-15, suppl. tome 1-6) front. (port., suppl. tome 1) plates (part. fold.) fold. maps, fold. tables. 26×20½ cm.

Title vignette, tome 1-3 title in red and black.

Author's names are given in tables of contents,

Bonar, p. 37.

No. of vols.:
16 vols and 6 supplementary vols.

Date: 1750.

tome 1-15.

Tome 1-15 have only general title-page; suppl.
tome 1-6 have general title-page which states subject of
special volume.

Imprint of tome 1-3: La Haye, P. de Hondt, 1750;
tome 4-15: new edition, Amsterdam, J. H. Schneider,
1766-71; suppl. tome 1-6: Amsterdam, J. H. Schneider,
1774-81.

Book plate: Adam Smith.

Contents:—Tome 1. De la manière d'étudier et de
traiter l'histoire naturelle. Histoire et théorie de la
terre. Par M. de Buffon. 1750.—Tome 2. Histoire naturelle des animaux. Histoire naturelle de l'homme.
Par M. de Buffon. 1750.—Tome 3. Description du
Cabinet du roy. Par M. Daubenton. 1750.—Tome
4-15. [Quadrapeds] Par M. de Buffon et M. Daubenton.
Nouv. éd. 1766-71.—Suppl. Tome 1-6. Par M. de
Buffon. Nouv. éd. 1774-81.

*Daubenton, Louis Jean Maries, 1716-1799, joint
author.*

The description of the Royal Cabinet of Natural
History by Buffon and Daubenton is referred to by
Adam Smith in Edinr. Rev. 1755, ii. p. 70, 71. See
Bonar, p. 37.

Also cf. W. of N. I. xi. p. 104; IV. vii. p. 251.

18. **Burch, Lambert van der,** 1542-1617.

Bonar, p. 162.

Heading:
Sabaudia

Sabavdiæ respvblica et historia. Lvgd. Batav., ex
officina Elzeviriana, 1634.

8 p.l., 313, [1]p. 11×5½ cm.

Engraved title-page.
Caption title: Lamberti van der-Bvrchii Sabavdorvm
origines, dvcvm principvm qve historiæ gentilitiæ.
Part of fly-leaf torn.

19. **Burke, Edmund,** 1729?-1797.

A philosophical enquiry into the origin of our
ideas of the sublime and beautiful. The 9th edition.
With an introductory discourse concerning taste, and
several other additions. London, printed for J. Dodsley, 1782.

ix, [7] 342 p. 21 cm.

Book plate: Adam Smith.

Bonar, p. 38.

20. —— *ditto* ——

Speech of Edmund Burke, Esq. On American
taxation, April 19, 1774. The 4th edition. London,
printed for J. Dodsley, 1775.

iv, 5-96 p. 21½ cm.

Book plate: Adam Smith.

With this are bound the author's "Speech... on
moving his resolutions for conciliations... (on 1775),
3. ed. 1778." "Speeches at his arrival at Bristol, and at
the conclusion of the poll. 2. ed. 1775." "Speech... to
the House of Commons (on... 1780), 4. ed. 1780." "A
letter... to J. Farr and J. Harris... on the affairs of
America. 4. ed. 1777." "Speech... upon certain points
relative to his parliamentary conduct. 5. ed. 1782."
"Speech... on Mr. Fox's East India bill. (on 1783),
1784."

Bonar, p. 37.

Entry:
  Speeches...
Date: 1782.

21. —— *ditto* ——

Speech of Edmund Burke, Esq. on moving his
resolutions for conciliation with the colonies, March
22, 1775. The 3rd edition. London, printed for J.
Dodsley, 1778.

2 p.l., 107 p. 21½ cm.

Bound with his "Speech... on American taxation.
4. ed. 1775."

Bonar,
*No separate en-
try.*

22. —— *ditto* ——

Mr. Edmund Burke's Speeches at his arrival at Bristol, and at the conclusion of the poll. The 2nd edition. London, printed for J. Dodsley, 1775.

vii, [3] 11-31 p. 21½ cm.

Bound with his "Speech... on American taxation. 4. ed. 1775."

Bonar,
No separate entry.

23. —— *ditto* ——

Speech of Edmund Burke, Esq. member of Parliament for the city of Bristol, on presenting to the House of Commons (on the 11th of February, 1780); a plan for the better security of the independence of Parliament, and the oeconomical reformation of the civil and other establishments. The 4th edition. London, printed for J. Dodsley, 1780.

2 p.l., 95 p. 21½ cm.

Bound with his "Speech... on American taxation. 4. ed. 1775."

Bonar,
No separate entry.

24. —— *ditto* ——

A letter from Edmund Burke, Esq.; one of the representatives in Parliament for the city of Bristol, to John Farr and John Harris, esqs. sheriffs of that city, on the affairs of America. The 4th ed. London, printed for J. Dodsley, 1777.

79 p. 21½ cm.

Bound with his "Speech... on American taxation. 4. ed. 1775."

Bonar,
No separate entry.

25. —— *ditto* ——

A speech of Edmund Burke, Esq. at the Guildhall, in Bristol, previous to the late election in that city, upon certain points relative to his parliamentary conduct.

Bonar,
No separate entry.

The 5th edition. London, printed for J. Dodsley, 1782.

2 p.l., 68 p. 21½ cm.

Bound with his "Speech... on American taxation. 4. ed. 1775."

26. ── *ditto* ──

Mr. Burke's Speech, on the 1st December 1783, upon the question for the speaker's leaving the chair, in order for the House to resolve itself into a committee on Mr. Fox's East India Bill. London, printed for J. Dodsley, 1784.

2 p.l., 105 p. 21½ cm.

Bound with his "Speech... on American taxation. 4. ed. 1775."

27. Burnet, Gilbert, *bp. of Salisbury*, 1643-1715.

The history of the reformation of the Church of England. The 3rd part. Being supplement to the two volumes formerly published. By the right reverend father in God, Gilbert Lord Bishop of Sarum. Dublin, printed by A. Rhames for R. Gunne [etc.] 1733.

2 p.l., xvi, 238, 10, 328, 8 p. ports. 32½ cm.

Title in red and black, initials, marginal notes.

Paged separately "A collection of records, letters and original paper."

Book plate: Adam Smith.

28. Busbecq, Ogier Chislain de, 1522-1592.

A. Gisleni Bvsbeqvii Omnia quæ extant... Amstelodami, ex officina Elzeviriana, 1660.

xl, 12-575, [23]p. 11×5½ cm.

Engraved title-page.

Margin notes:

Bonar, No separate entry.

Bonar, p. 39.

Bonar, p. 39.
Heading: Busbequius.
Date: 1600.

Book plate: Adam Smith.

Ms. on title-page: A. Fletcher.

Contents:—I. Avgerii Gislenii Bvsbequii Legatio-nis-Turcicæ epistolæ quatuor. —II. Ejusdem exclama-tio, sive de re militari contra Turcam instituenda con-silium. —III. Solimanni Turcarum Imp. Legatio ad Ferdinandum Roman. Cæs., anno 1542. —IV. Ejus-dem Busbequii, Cæsaris apud Regem Gallorum Legati, epistolæ ad Rudolphum II.

29. **Bussy-Castelnau, Charles Joseph Patissier, marquis de,** 1718-1785.

Bonar, *No entry*.

Mémoire à consulter et consultation, pour le sieur de Bussy maréchal des camps & armées du roi; au sujet du Mémoire que le sieur de Lally, lieutenant général, vient de répandre dans le public. Avec les lettres que les sieurs de Bussy & de Lally se sont écrites dans l'Inde, pour servir de pièces justificatives. A Paris, de l'Imprimerie de M. Lambert, 1766.

iv, 69, [3] xxiv, 258 p.

Bound with "Mémoire pour le comte de Lally..."

Ms. on the verso of title-page.

30. **Carte, Thomas,** 1686-1754.

Bonar, p. 42.

A general history of England... By Thomas Carte, an Englishman. London, printed for the author, 1747 55.

4 v. geneal. table. 38½×24 cm.

Vol. 1: Printed for the author, and sold by J. H. Hodges; vols. 2-4: Printed for W. Russel.

"Names of authors cited": vol. 1, pp. xii-xvi.

Book plate: Adam Smith.

Contents:—Vol. 1. An account of the first in-habitants of the country, and the transactions in it, from the earliest times to the death of King John, A.D.

1216. —Vol. 2. An account of all public transactions from the accession of Henry III, A.D. 1216. to the death of Henry VII, April 21, A.D. 1509. —Vol. 3. An account of all public transactions from the accession of Henry VIII, A.D. 1509, to the marriage of the Elector Palatine with the Princess Elizabeth, daughter of James I, in A.D. 1613. —Vol. 4. An account of all public transactions from the marriage of the Elector Palatine with the Princess Elizabeth, A.D. 1613, to A.D. 1654, about five years before the Restoration.

31. Chalmers, George, 1742-1825, *ed.*

Bonar, p. 43.

Political annals of the present united colonies, from their settlement to the peace of 1763; compiled chiefly from records, and authorised often by the insertion of state-papers... By George Chalmers, Esq. Book I. London, printed for the author and sold by J. Bowen, 1780.

5 p.l., 695 p. 29½×24 cm.

No more published in separate form.

Book plate: Adam Smith.

Bk. I. contains political annals of these colonies from their settlement to the revolution of 1688. Bk. II., which should have covered the periods 1688-1763, not published.

George Chalmers was the author of "An Estimate of the Comparative Strength of Britain during the present and four preceding reigns and of the Losses of her Trade from every War since the Revolution... London, 1782" and he requested "Dr. Adam Smith to accept of this enlarged and corrected copy of his Estimate as a mark of his high respect." See Bonar, p. 43.

32. Chaucer, Geoffrey, *d.* 1400.

Bonar, p. 45.

The works of Geoffrey Chaucer, compared with the former editions, and many valuable mss. out of

which, three tales are added which were never before
printed; by John Urry, student of Christ-Church, Oxon.
deceased: together with a glossary, by a student of the
same college. To the whole is prefixed the author's
life, newly written, and a preface, giving an account
of this edition. London, printed for B. Lintot, 1721.

26 p.l., 626, 81, [1]p. front., illus., port. 40½ cm.

Title vignette.

Book plate: Adam Smith.

*The work was left unfinished at Urry's death, and
the revision and completion were intrusted to Timothy
Thomas, who wrote the preface and glossary.*

*The life of Chaucer was originally written by John
Dart, but was revised and altered by William Thomas.*

*The three tales mentioned in the title are The
coke's tale of Gamelyn; The merchant's second tale, or
The history of Beryn; and The adventure of the
pardoner and tapster at the Inn at Canterbury.*

Urry, John, 1666-1715.
Thomas, Timothy, 1692?-1751.
Dart, John, d. 1730.
Thomas, William, fl. 1721.

*Adam Smith referred to "Chaucer, the father of
the English Poetry" in Essays, p.150; On the Imitative Arts. See Bonar, p. 45.*

33. Chiabrera, Gabriello, 1552-1638.

Delle opere di Gabriello Chiabrera in questa ultima
impressione tutte in un corpo novellamente unite...
In Venezia, presso G. Pasquali, 1771-82.

6 v. port. 15½ cm.

Title vignette.

"Vita di Gabriello Chiabrera, Savonese, da lui
medesimo scritta" vol.1, pp. xvi-xli.

Imprint of vol. 6: Venezia, nella Stamperia Coleti,

Bonar, p. 45.

Imprint:
Editors 1–5
Giuseppe Pa-
squali, 6 Co-
leti.

1771.

Book plate: Adam Smith.

Contents:—1. Le canzoni-eroiche, le lugueri, le morali, e le sagre. —2. Le canzonette amorose, e morali, scherzi, sonetti, epistaffj, vendemmie, egloghe, e sermoni. —3. Poemetti profani, e sacri. —4. Le poesie liriche... —5. Altri componimenti in verso, ed in prosa non più raccolti, e nelle passate edizioni non compresi... —6. Delle guerre de' Goti... Cogli argomenti del signor dottore Antonio Frizzi...

34. **Choisy, François Timoléon, abbé de**, 1644-1724.

Bonar, p. 46.

Imprint:
15th ed.

Mémoires pour servir à l'histoire de Louis XIV, par feu M. l'abbé de Choisy... 5me édition, revûë, corrigée & augmentée. A Utrecht, Chez Van-de-Water, 1727.

3 v. in 1. xiv, 191, 177, 199 p. 17 cm.

Title-page vol.1 only, title in red and black.

Book plate: Adam Smith.

35. **Clarendon, Edward Hyde, 1st earl of,**
1609-1674.

Bonar, p. 47.

[The life of Edward, earl of Clarendon...] written by himself. The 3rd edition. Oxford, at the Clarendon printing-house, 1761.

2v. (vol.2 and 3 only) 21 cm.

Vol.1 has general and special title-page; vol.2 and 3 have special title-pages only: "The continuation of the life of Edward earl of Clarendon, lord high chancellor of England, and chancellor of the University of Oxford. Being a continuation of his History of the grand rebellion, from the restoration to his banishment in 1667. Written by himself. Printed from his original manuscripts, given to the University of Oxford by the heirs of the late Earl of Clarendon... the 3rd edition. Oxford, at the Clarendon Printing-house, 1761." Paged continuously.

Book plate: Adam Smith.

Lord Clarendon is mentioned by Adam Smith in Mor. Sent. Pt. VI. Sect. III. See Bonar, p. 47.

36. **Commines, Philippe de,** *sieur d'Argenton,*
    1445?-1511.

Bonar, p. 49.

Les memoires de messire Philippe de Commines, chevalier, seignevr d'Argenton, svr les principavx faicts & gestes de Louis onziesme & de Charles huictiesme son fils Roys de France. Revevs et corrigez par Denis Savuage de Fontenailles... A Paris, pour A. L'Angelier, 1580.

6 p.l., 341, 6 p. 33½ cm.

Printer's device on title-page, initials; head and tail pieces.

Book plate: Adam Smith.

Sauvage, Denis, sieur du Pare, 1520?-1587?

37. **A complete history of England**: with the lives of all the kings and queens, thereof; from the earliest account of time, to the death of His late Majesty King William III. Containing a faithful relation of all affairs of state, ecclesiastical and civil. The whole illustrated with large and useful notes, taken from divers manuscripts, and other good authors: and the effigies of the kings and queens... with alphabetical indexes... London, printed for B. Aylmer [etc.] 1706.

Bonar, p. 65.

Heading:
   England.

3 v. 28 ports. (incl. fronts., vol. 1, 3) 40 cm.
Title in red and black.

Book plate: Adam Smith; pasted on another.

Ms. notes on fly-leaf, vol. 1 and 2: John Ormsby his book.

Contents:—Vol. 1. I. Beginning with the history of Britain to William the Conqueror, by John Milton.

—II. From the conquest to the end of King Edward III., by Samuel Daniel. —III. The reigns of King Richard II., King Henry IV., V., and VI., all new writ in Mr. Daniel's method. —IV. The reign of King Edward IV., by John Habington. —V. The lives of King Edward V., and Richard III., by Sir Thomas Moore, translated from the latin original. —VI. The life of King Richard III., by George Buck. —VII. The life of King Henry VII., by Francis lord Bacon. Vol. 2. I. The history of King Henry VIII., written by Edward lord Herbert of Cherbury. —II. The life of King Edward VI., by Sir John Hayward. —III. The life of Queen Mary, written in Latin by Francis Godwin, lord bishop of Hereford, newly translated into English by J. H. —IV. The history of Queen Elizabeth, written by William Cambden, newly done into English. —V. The annals of King James I., by the said Mr. Cambden. —VI. The history of King James I., by Arthur Wilson. Vol. 3. I. The history and life of King Charles I. —II. [The history] of King Charles II. —III. [The history] of King James II. —IV. [The history] of King William and Queen Mary. —V. [The history] of King William III. All new writ by a learned and impartial hand White Kennett.

In 1706 John Hughes collected the materials for the first two volumes; the third volume was written by White Kennett, bishop of Peter borough, by whose name this history is generally known.

Numerous notes contributed by John Strype.

Kennett, White, bp. of Peter borough, 1660-1728. Hughes, John, 1677-1720. Strype, John, 1643-1737.

38. **Cordiner, Charles,** 1746?-1794.

Bonar, p. 50.

Antiquities & scenery of the north of Scotland, in a series of letters, to Thomas Pennant, Esq. by the Revd. Chas. Cordiner, Minister of St. Andrew's

Place of publication:
Banff [sic]

Chapel, Bamff. London, 1780.

> 1 p.l., 173, [11]p. xxi pl. (1 fold.) 24 cm.

> Engraved title-page.

> "Designed as a supplement to Pennant's Scotish tour."—Lowndes.

> Extracts from the "Orcades" of Torfæus: pp. 121-173.

> Book plate: Adam Smith.

> *Inserted a crown paper with handwritten genealogical table.*

> *Torfæus, Thormodus; who wrote a history of Scotland.*

39. **Cowley, Abraham,** 1618-1667.   Bonar, p. 50.

> The works of Mr. Abraham Cowley. Consisting of those which were formerly printed: and those which be design'd 'for the press. Now published out of the author's original copies. To this edition are added, Cutter of Coleman-street: and several commendatory copies of verses on the author, by persons of honour. As also, a table to the whole works, never before printed. The 8th edition. London, printed for H. Herringman; and are to be sold by R. Bentley, J. Tonson [etc.] 1693, 1681.

> 2 v. in 1. front. (vol. 1, port.) 29 cm.

> Vol. 2 has title: The second part of the works of Mr. Abraham Cowley. Being what was written and published by himself in his younger years, and now reprinted together. The 4th edition. London, printed by M. Clark, for C. Harper... 1681.

> "An account of the life and writings of Mr. Abraham Cowley." (vol. 1, [24]p.) by T. Sprat.

> The Mistress, Pindarique odes, Davideis, Cutter of Coleman-street, vol. 1, have separate paging and special title-pages.

> The second part, the tragical history of Piramus

and Thisbe, Sylva, Love's riddle, Naufragium joculare, vol. 2, have separate title-pages.

Book plate: Adam Smith.

Cowley, Abraham, a poet, loyal to King's cause during the Civil War.

Sprat, Thomas, bp. of Rochester, 1635-1713.

Cowley is referred to in Mor. Sent. Pt. I. Sect. II. ch. ii., and Edinr. Rev. 1755-56, I. 64. See Bonar, p. 51.

40. **Crawfurd, George,** *d.* 1748.

The lives and characters, of the officers of the crown, and of the state in Scotland, from the beginning of the reign of King David I. to the union of the two Kingdoms. Collected from original charters, chartularies, authentick records, and the most approved histories. To which is added, an appendix, containing several original papers relating to the lives, and referring to them. By George Crawfurd, esq; Vol. I. Edinburgh, printed by R. Fleming and company, and sold by J. M'Euen, 1726.

6 p.l., 480 p. 33 cm.

No more published.

Title vignette, initials, head and tail pieces.

Book plate: Adam Smith.

Bonar, p. 51.

Heading:
Crawford.

41. **[Defoe, Daniel]** 1661?-1731.

The history of the union of Great Britain. Edinburgh, printed by the heirs and successors of A. Anderson, 1709.

8 p.l., xxxii, 60, 116, 273, [1] 38, 131 p. 31½ cm.

Dedications signed by the author.
Title vignette.
Book plate: Adam Smith.

Ms. notes on fly-leaf: Ex libris Johannes J? odd Emptum er Gulielmo Drickie pictium 12 gro? Ex libris John Todhisboob. David.

Bonar, p. 83.

Heading:
History of
the Union.

42. Diderot, Denis, 1713-1784.   Bonar, p. 56.

Œuvres philosophiques et dramatiques de M. Diderot... Amsterdam, 1772.

Vol.3, 4, 6 only. xi fold. pl. 16¾ cm.
Each article has special title-page and paging.
Initials and head pieces.

Book plate: Adam Smith.

Contents:—Tome 3. Pensées sur l'interpétation de la nature. Pensées philosophiques. Traité du beau. La philosophie des chinois. —Tome 4. Le fils naturel, ou les épreuves de la vertu, comédie, avec l'Histoire véritable de la pièce. —Tome 6. Mémoires sur différens sujets de mathématiques.

Diderot is mentioned by Adam Smith in Edinr. Rev. 1755, ii. p.66, 68. See Bonar, p.57.

43. Dryden, John, 1631-1700.   Bonar, p. 60.

The miscellaneous works of John Dryden, esq; containing all his original poems, tales, and translations... With explanatory notes and observations. Also an account of his life and writings. London, printed for J. & R. Tonson, 1760.

4 v. illus., ports. 20½ cm.

Vol. 1, Dedication signed: Samuel Derrick, 1760. "The life of John Dryden, Esq." vol. 1, ⌊xiii⌋-xxxiv. Vol. 2, Preface by John Dryden. Vol. 3, Dedication signed: John Dryden, 1699.

Book plate: Adam Smith.

Dryden is referred to in Mor. Sent. Pt. V. ch. i, and Edinr. Rev. 1755, p. 64. See Bonar, p. 60.

44. Dyer, John, 1700?-1757.   Bonar, p. 64.

Poems. By John Dyer, LL.B. Viz. I. Grongar

Hill. II. The ruins of Rome. III. The fleece, in four books. London, printed for J. Dodsley, 1770.

v, 9-190 p. incl. 2 pl. 18 cm.

Book plate: Adam Smith.

45. Euclides.

The elements of Euclid, viz. The first six books, together with the eleventh and twelfth. The errors, by which Theon, or others, have long ago vitiated these books, are corrected, and some of Euclid's demonstrations are restored. Also the book of Euclid's data, in like manner corrected. By Robert Simson, M.D. Emeritus Professor of Mathematics in the University of Glasgow... Glasgow, printed and sold by A. Foulis [etc., etc.] 1781.

4 p.l., 466, [2] 32 p. diagrs. (part. fold.) 21½ cm.

"Notes critical and geometrical": pp. [287]-466 have special title-page.

"The elements of plane and spherical trigonometry": have special title-page, and paging.

Book plate: Adam Smith.

Ms. notes on pp. 7-13, 43, 44.

Simson, Robert, 1687-1768, ed.
Dr. Robert Simson is called by Adam Smith as one of "the two greatest mathematicians that I ever have had the honour to be known to, and I believe the two greatest that have lived in my time." Mor. Sent. Pt. III. ch. ii. See Bonar, pp. 167-168.

46. Fordun, John, *d.* 1384?

Johannis de Fordun Scotichronicon, cum supplementis et continuatione Walteri Boweri Insulæ Sancti Columbæ Abbatis. E codicibus MSS. editum. Cum notis et variantibus lectionibus. Edinburgi, Typis et impensis R. Flaminii, 1747.

Bonar, p. 167.

Heading:
Simson.

Bonar, p. 70.

2 v. 30½ cm.

Book plate: Adam Smith.

"De nuptiis Roberti Senescalli Scotiae atque Eliza-
bethae Morae dissertatio. 1749," prefixed to vol. ii.

47. **Gesner, Johann Matthias,** 1691-1761.

Scriptores rei rvsticae veteres latini Cato, Varro,
Colvmella, Palladivs, quibvs nvnc accedit vegetivs de
Mvlo-Medicina et Gargilii martialis fragmentvm cvm
editionibvs prope omnibvs et MSS. plvribvs collati:
adiectae notae virorvm clariss. integrae tvm editae tvm
ineditae et lexicon rei rvsticae cvrante Io. Matthia
Gesnero. Editio secvnda. Lipsiae, Svmtibvs C. Fritsch.
1773-74.

2 v. front., fold. pl. 25 cm.

Book plate: Adam Smith.

Columella, Palladius and Varro are referred to in
W. of N. Cannan's ed. I. p. 154, 155.

48. **Gilles, Pierre,** 1490-1555.

P. Gyllii de Constantinopoleos topographia lib.
IV. Lugduni Batavorum, ex officina Elzeviriana, 1632.

7 p.l., 15-422, [6]p. 11×5½ cm.

Engraved title-page.
Edited by Antoine Gilles.

49. **Giovio, Paolo,** *bp. of Nocera,* 1483-1552.

Pavli Iovii... Historiarvm svi temporis tomvs
primvs [-secvndvs]... cvm indice plenissimo. Lvtetiæ
Parisiorum, ex officina M. Vascosani, 1553-54.

2 v. in 1. 34½ cm.

Each volume has special title-page.
Initials.

Book plate: Adam Smith.

Bonar, p. 2.

Heading:
  Agriculture.

Date: 1773.

Bonar, p. 75.

Heading:
  Gesnerus.

Date: 1773.

Bonar, p. 80.

Heading:
  Gyllius, Pe-
  trus.

Bonar, p. 188.

Heading:
  Turkey.

Bonar, p. 139.

Heading:
  Pavlus Jovi-
  us.

Date: 1553.

Ms. on title-page and fly-leaf: Ex libris Colini Campbell, 1604; *etc.*

50. **Grew, Nehemiah,** 1641-1712.

Bonar, p. 78.

The anatomy of plants. With An idea of a philosophical history of plants, and several other lectures, read before the Royal Society. By Nehemjah Grew... [London] printed by W. Rawlins, for the author, 1682.

11 p.l., 24, [10] 304 (i.e. 300) [19]p. 83 pl. (part. fold.) 32 cm.

Each work has special title-page.

Book plate: Adam Smith.

Contents:—An idea of a philosophical history of plants. 2nd ed. 1st book: General account of vegetation. 2nd ed. 2nd book: The anatomy of roots. 2nd ed. 3rd book: The anatomy of trunks. 2nd ed. 4th book: The anatomy of leaves, flowers, fruits and seeds. Several lectures: 1. Of the nature, causes, and power of mixture. 2nd ed. 2. Of the luctation arising upon the mixture of several menstruum's with all sorts of bodies. 2nd ed. 3. An essay of the various proportions, wherein lixivial salts are found in plants. 4. Of the essential and marine salts of plants. 5. Of the colours of plants. 6. Of the diversities and causes of tasts; chiefly in plants. With an appendix, of the odours of plants. 7. Experiments in consort, upon the solution of salts in water.

51. **Harris, John,** 1667?-1719.

Bonar, p. 81.

Navigantium atque itinerantium bibliotheca. Or, A complete collection of voyages and travels. Consisting of above six hundred of the most authentic writers... Originally published... by John Harris... Now carefully revised, with large additions, and continued down to the present time; including particular accounts of the manufactures and commerce of each country... London, printed for T. Osborne [etc.] 1764.

2 v. front. (vol. 2) plates, ports., maps (part. fold.) 42½ cm.

Title in red and black.
Edited by John Campbell.
1st edition, London, 1705.

Book plate: Adam Smith.

Dedication: To the merchants of Great Britain, by the author, 1745.

Contents:

Vol. 1. ch. I. The History of the circum-navigators. ch. II. Comprehending the discovery, settlement, and commerce of the East-Indies.

Vol. 2. Bk. I. An account of the circum-navigators of the globe, and of the discoveries of the East and West, and West-Indies. —Bk. II. Voyages and discoveries towards the north, and through most of the countries of Europe. —Bk. III. Voyages to, and travels through the dominions of the Grand Signior, and through the other empires, kingdoms and states in Asia; with curious and copious accounts of such parts of that great continent as are least known.

52. Harte, Walter, 1709-1774.   Bonar, p. 81.

Essays on husbandry. Essay I. A general introduction, shewing, that agriculture is the basis and support of all flourishing communities;—the antient and present state of that useful art;—agriculture, manufactures, trade, and commerce justly harmonized;—of the right cultivation of our colonies;—together with the defects, omissions, and possible improvements in English husbandry. Essay II. An account of some experiments tending to improve the culture of lucerne by transplantation... The whole illustrated with five copper-plates, and twenty-five representations cut on wood... The 2nd edition, corrected and enlarged. By the Revd. Walter Harte... London, printed for W. Frederick [etc.], 1770.

xxvi, [2] 213, 232, [2]p. illus., v pl. 20½ cm.

"List of writers": pp. xxi-xxvi.

Book plate: Adam Smith.

53. **Helvetiorum respublica.** Diversorum autorum quorum nonnulli nunc primum in lucem prodeunt. Lugd. Bat., ex officina Elzeviriana, 1627.

535, [17]p. 11½×5½ cm.

Engraved title-page.

Bound with "Belgii confederati respublica... 1630." by J. de Laet.

54. **Herbelot de Molainville, Barthélemy d',** 1625-1695.

Bibliothèque orientale, ou Dictionnaire universel, contenant généralement tout ce qui regarde la connoissance des peuples de l'Orient. Leurs histoires et traditions véritables ou fabuleuses; leurs religions, sectes et politique, leurs gouvernement, loix, coutumes, mœurs, guerres, & les révolutions de leurs empires; leurs sciences et leurs arts, leur théologie, mythologie, magie... les vies et actions remarquables de tous leurs saints, docteurs, philosophes, historiens, poëtes, capitaines, & de tous ceux qui se sont rendus illustres parmi eux, par leur vertu, ou par leur savoir; des jugements critiques, et des extraits de tous leurs ouvrages ... Par monsieur d'Herbelot. A Maestricht, Chez J. E. Dufour & Ph. Roux, 1776.

1 p.l., xxi, 22-26, 954 p. 42½ cm.

Title in red and black, title vignette; head and tail pieces.

Book plate: Adam Smith.

1st ed., Paris, 1697.

This work based mainly upon "Lexicon biblio-graphicum et enciclopedicum" of Haji Khalfah.

P. iii-xxi, Discours pour servir de préface à la Bibliothéque orientale, signed by A. Galand.

Galland, Antoine, 1646-1715.

55. [**Herd, David**] 1732-1810, *ed.*

Ancient and modern Scottish songs, heroic ballads, etc. in 2 vols... Edinburgh, printed by J. Wotherspoon for J. Dickson and C. Elliot, 1776.

Vol. 1 only. 17½ cm.

Title vignette.
Published anonymously.

Book plate: Adam Smith.

A reference to Scottish poetry occurs in Essays: "On Imitative Arts," p. 182, 183. See Bonar, pp. 164-165.

56. **Hobbes, Thomas,** 1588-1679.

Leviathan; or, The matter, forme, & power of a common-wealth ecclesiasticall and civill. By Thomas Hobbes of Malmesbury. London, printed for A. Crooke, 1651.

3 p.l., 396 p. fold. table. 28 cm.

With engraved added title-page.

Book plate: Adam Smith.
Ms. notes in dedication, introduction, etc.

Hobbes is quoted by Adam Smith in Mor. Sent. Part VII. Sect. III. ch. i. and ch. ii.; W. of N. I. vol. 15. 1.; Edinr. Rev. 1755, Part II. July; and Lectures p. 2. See Bonar, pp. 83-84.

Bonar, p. 164.

Heading: Scotland.

Bonar, p. 83.

57. —— *ditto* ——

Bonar, p. 83.

The moral and political works of Thomas Hobbes, of Malmesbury. Never before collected together. To which is prefixed, the author's life, extracted from that said to be written by himself, as also from the supplement to the said life by Dr. Blackbourne, and farther illustrated by the editor, with historical and critical remarks on his writings and opinions. London, 1750.

xxviii, 697, [3]p. port. 37 cm.

Engraved added title-page: Leviathan: or The matter, form, and power of a common wealth, ecclesiastical and civil. Written by Tho. Hobbes. 1651.

Book plate: Adam Smith.

58. **Huggan, John.**

Bonar, p. 89.

Dissertatio medica inauguralis de sanguine humano, ejusque missionis usu ac abusu. Quam... ex auctoritate... Gulielmi Robertson... Academiæ edinburgenæ præfecti... pro gradu doctoris... eruditorum examini subjicit Joannes Huggan, Britannus. Ad diem 12 junii [1771]... Edinburgi, apud Balfour, Auld, et Smellie, academiae, typographos, 1771.

61 p. 20 cm.

Book plate: Adam Smith.

59. **Hume, David,** *of Godscroft,* 1560?-1630?

Bonar, p. 89.

A general history of Scotland, from the year 767 to the death of King James: containing the principal revolutions and trans-actions of church & state: with political observations and reflections upon the same. By David Hume of Godscroft. London, printed for S. Miller, 1657.

9 p.l., 440 (i.e. 450) p. 28½ cm.

Head pieces and engraved initials, marginal notes.

Page no. 205-214 duplicated.

Un-numbered p. 213 is special title-page: The second part of the history of the Douglasses, containing the House of Angus. By master David Hume of Godscroft. Edinburgh, printed by E. Tyler, 1643.

Book plate: Adam Smith.
Upper part of 2nd leaf torn.

60. Hume, David, 1711-1776.   Bonar, p. 90.

Essays and treatises on several subjects... By David Hume, Esq... A new edition. London, printed for T. Cadell [etc.] 1770.

4 v. 15½ cm.

Book plate: Adam Smith.

Contents:—Vol. 1, 2. Essays, moral, political, and literary. —Vol. 3. An enquiry concerning human understanding; and A dissertation on the passions. —Vol. 4. An enquiry concerning the principles of morals; and The natural history of religion.

Vol. 3 contains pages with handwritten vertical lines.

Hume is frequently quoted by Adam Smith. See Bonar, pp. 90-91.

61. —— *ditto* ——   Bonar, p. 90.

Essays and treatises on several subjects... By David Hume, Esq... A new edition. London, printed for T. Cadell [etc.] 1777.

2 v. 22 cm.

Book plate: Adam Smith.

Contents:—Vol. 1. Essays, moral, political, and literary. —Vol. 2. An enquiry concerning human understanding. A dissertation on the passions. An enquiry concerning the principles of morals. The natural history of religion.

62. —— *ditto* ——

Bonar, p. 90.

The history of England, from the invasion of Julius Cæsar to the revolution in 1688... By David Hume, Esq... A new edition, with the author's last corrections and improvements. To which is prefixed, a short account of his life, written by himself. London, printed for T. Cadell, 1778.

8 v. front. (port.) 22 cm.

"Letter from Adam Smith, LL.D. to William Strahan, Esq." pp. [xvii]-xxiii.

Book plate: Adam Smith.

In "Letter to William Strahan", Adam Smith wrote, "Thus died out most excellent, and never to be forgotten friend;... Upon the whole, I have always considered him, both in his life time and since his death, as approaching as nearly to the idea of a perfectly wise and virtuous man, as perhaps the nature of human frailty will permit."

63. —— *ditto* ——

Bonar, p. 89.

A treatise on human nature: being an attempt to introduce the experimental method of reasoning into moral subjects... London, printed for J. Noon, 1739.

Vol. 1 only (vol. 2 and 3 wanting) 21 cm.

With marginal notes.
Published anonymously.

Book plate: Adam Smith.

64. Jesuits.

Bonar, p. 95.

Entry:
  Pièces sur les Jésuites.

Date: 1760.

Recueil de toutes les pieces et nouvelles qui ont paru sur les affaires des Jésuites, principalement dans l'Amérique méridionale, & dans le royaume de Portugal. 1760-61.

4 v. 17¼ cm.

Head and tail pieces.

Vol. 3 and 4 contain: "Nouvelles intéressantes au sujet de l'attentat commis le 3 septembre 1758, sur la personne sacrée de Sa Majesté très-fidele, le roi de Portugal." "Recueil des actes émanés des secrétaireries d'état de Rome & de Lisbonne, pendant le tems qu'a duré le négociation entre les deux cours, c'est-à-dire depuis le 20 avril 1759 jusqu'au mois d'août 1760, au sujet du bref de commission demandé par le roi très-fidele pour son tribunal royal de conscience ou des ordres. Traduit du portugais, imprimé à la secrétaire-rie d'état par ordre exprès de Sa Majesté très-fidéle 1761." vol. 4, with special title-page and paging.

Book plate: Adam Smith.

65. Johnson, Samuel, 1709-1784.

Bonar, p. 95.

The lives of the most eminent English poets; with critical observations on their works. By Samuel Johnson... London, printed for C. Bathurst, J. Buckland [etc., etc.] 1781.

4 v. front. (port.) 21½ cm.

Book plate: Adam Smith.

Contents: —Vol. 1. Cowley. Denham. Milton. Butler. Rochester. Roscommon. Otway. Waller. Pomfret. Dorset. Stepney. Philips. Walsh. —Vol. 2. Dryden. Smith. Duke. King. Sprat. Halifax. Parnell. Garth. Rowe. Addison. Huches. Sheffield. —Vol. 3. Prior. Congreve. Blackmore. Fenton. Gay. Granville. Yalden. Tickell. Hammond. Somervile. Savage. Swift. Broome. —Vol. 4. Pope. Pitt. Thomson. Watts. A. Philips. West. Collins. Dyer. Shenstone. Young. Waller. Akenside. Gray. Lyttelton.

66. —— *ditto* ——

Bonar, p. 95.

Prayers and meditations, composed by Samuel Johnson, LL.D., and published from his manuscripts, by George Strahan... London, printed for T. Cadell, 1785.

xvi, 227, [1]p. 21½ cm.

Book plate: Adam Smith.

67. Koran.

Le Coran, traduit de l'Arabe, accompagné de notes, et précédé d'un abrégé de la vie de Mahomet, tiré des écrivains orientaux les plus estimés. Par M. Savary. A Paris, Chez Knapen & fils, & Onfroy, 1783.

2 v. 20½ cm.

Head and tail pieces.

Book plate: Adam Smith.

Savary, Claude Etiennes, 1750-1788, tr.

68. La Bruyère, Jean de, 1645-1696.

Les caracteres de Theophraste traduits du grec; avec Les caracteres ou les moeurs de ce siecle. Par Mr. de La Bruyere... et la clef, en marge & par ordre alphabétique. A Paris, Chez E. Michallet, 1697.

2 v. front. 16½ cm.

Head pieces, marginal notes.

Book plate: Adam Smith.

69. La Condamine, Charles Marie de, 1701-1774.

Journal of a tour to Italy... By M. de la Condamine. London, printed for T. Lewis, and G. Kearsly, 1763.

xxii, [2]235, [1]p. 17½ cm.

Book plate: Adam Smith.

Contents:—An Account of the Eruptions of Mount Vesuvius.—Of the Curiosities discovered at Herculanum.—Of the leaning Towers of Pisa and Bologna, etc.

The author was a French scientist and philosopher.

70. **[La Curne de Sainte-Palaye, Jean Baptiste de]** 1697-1781.

Histoire littéraire des Troubadours, contenant leurs vies, les extraits de leurs pièces, & plusieurs particularités sur les mœurs, les usages, & l'histoire du douzième & du treizième siècles... A Paris, Chez Durand neveu, 1774.

3 v. 17½ cm.

Head and tail pieces.
Published anonymously, by Claude François Xavier Millot, 1726-1785.

Book plate: Adam Smith.

Bonar, p. 187.

Heading:
Troubadours.

71. **Laet, Joannes de,** 1593-1649.

Belgii confœderati respublica: sev Gelriæ. Holland. Zeland. Traject. Fris. Transisal. Groning. chorographica politicaque descriptio... Lvgd. Batav., ex officina Elzeviriana, 1630.

7 p.l., 352, [9]p. 11½×5½ cm.

Engraved title-page.
Introduction signed: J. de Laet.

With this is bound "Helvetorium respublica... 1627."

Bonar, p. 21.

Heading:
Belgium Confederatum.

72. —— *ditto* ——

Gallia, sive De Francorvm regis dominiis et opibus commentarius. Lvgdvni Batavorvm, ex officina Elzeviriana, 1629.

8 p.l., 461, [1]p. 11½×5½ cm.

Engraved title-page.
Dedication signed: Joannes de Laet.

Bonar, p. 98.

[Not listed as J.]

73. —— [*ditto*] ——

Bonar, p. 98.

De imperio Magni Mogolis, sive India vera commentarius. E varijs auctoribus congestus... Lvgdvni
Batavorvm, ex officina Elzeviriana, 1631.

6 p.l., 299, [17]p. 11×5½ cm.

Engraved title-page.
Dedication signed: Joannes de Laet.

74. —— [*ditto*] ——

Bonar, p. 177.

Heading:
  Spain.

Hispania, sive De regis Hispaniæ regnis et opibus
commentarius. Lvgd. Batav., ex officina Elzeviriana,
1629.

8 p.l., 498, [1]p. 11½×5½ cm.

Engraved title-page.
Dedication signed: Joannes de Laet.

A fly leaf with manuscript torn.

75. La Fontaine, Jean de, 1621-1695.

Bonar, p. 70.

[Not listed as
J.]

Fables choisies, mises en vers, par monsieur de La
Fontaine, avec la vie d'Esope. Nouvelle édition, aug-
mentée de petites nottes pour en faciliter l'intelligence.
A Amsterdam, Chez l'Honoré et Chatelain, 1722.

xlvii, [1] 482, [44]p. front. 17 cm.

Title in red and black, title vignette, head and tail
pieces, initials.

Book plate: Adam Smith.

*La Fontaine is referred to in Mor. Sent. Part III.
ch. ii. See* Bonar, p. 70.

76. La Fosse, Antoine de, *sieur d'Aubigny,*
1653-1708.

Bonar, p. 70.

[Not listed as
J.]

Les œuvres de monsieur de La Fosse, nouvelle
édition, revue, corrigée et augmentée de ses poésies

diverses... A Paris, par la Compagnie des libraires associés, 1747.

Vol. 2 only.   17 cm.

Title in red and black, title vignette, head and tail pieces, initials.

77. **Lally, Thomas Arthur, *baron de Tolendal*, *comte de*, 1702-1766.**

Bonar, p. 113
Heading:
Mémoire.

Mémoire pour le comte de Lally, lieutenant-général des Armées du roi,... commissaire du roi & commandant en chef dans l'Inde. Contre monsieur le Procureur-général. A Paris, de l'imprimerie de G. Desprez, 1766.

2. p.l., 300, 138, 51 p. 26 cm.

With this is bound: Mémoire à consulter et consultation, pour le sieur De Bussy... au sujet du Mémoire que le sieur de Lally, lieutenant général, vient de répandre dans le public... Paris, Michel Lambert, 1766.

Book plate: Adam Smith.

Ms. on fly-leaf.

Lally lost war in India, was made prisoner and executed in 1760.

78. **Leo Africanus, Joannes, *16th cent.***

Bonar, p. 100.

Joannis Leonis Africani Africae descriptio IX. lib. absoluta. Lugd. Batav., apud Elzevir, 1632.

2 pt. in 1 v. 11½×5½ cm.

Engraved title-page.
Paged continuously: 800, [16]p. incl. title-pages.
Part 2 has title: Johannis Leonis Africani de Africæ descriptione, pars altera. Lvgdvni Batavorvm, ex officinâ Elzeviriana, 1632.

79. **Le Vassor, Michel,** 1646-1718.

Histoire du regne de Louis XIII, roi de France et de Navarre... Par Mr. Michel le Vassor... A Amsterdam, Chez Z. Chatelain, 1732-51.

10 v. in 18. front., plates (port.) 15½ cm.

Added title-page engraved, title in red and black, title vignette, head and tail pieces, marginal notes.

Book plate: Adam Smith.

Tome I, dernière éd., revuë et plus exactment corrigée que les précédentes, 1750; tome II, in 2 pt., nouv. éd., 1751; tome III, in 2 pt., nouv. éd., 1733; tome IV, nouv. éd., 1751; tome V, nouv. éd., 1751; tome VI, in 2 pt., nouv. éd., 1734; tome VII, in 2 pt., nouv. éd., 1751; tome VIII, in 2 pt., 3. éd., 1732; tome IX, in 2 pt., nouv. éd., 1735; tome X, in 2 pt., nouv. éd., 1751.

Bonar, p. 190.

No. of vols.: 10

Date: 1735
[Not listed as J.]

80. —— *ditto* ——

Caroli v. Linné... Genera plantarum eorumque characteres naturales secundum numerum, figuram, situm, et proportionem omnium fructificationis partium. Editio novissima. Viennæ, typis J. Thomae nob. de Trattnern, 1767.

2 p.l., xix, [1] 580, [44]p. 20 cm.

Book plate: Adam Smith.

Bonar, p. 101.

81. —— *ditto* ——

Caroli Linnæi... Philosophia botanica in qua explicantur fundamenta botanica cum definitionibus partium, exemplis terminorum, observationibus rariorum, adjectis figuris æneis... Stockholmiæ, apud Godofr. Kiesewetter, 1751.

3 p.l., 362 p. front. (port.) illus., x pl. 20½ cm.

Book plate: Adam Smith.

Bonar, p. 101.

82. —— *ditto* ——
Bonar, p. 101.

Caroli Linnæi... Species plantarum, exhibentes plantas rite cognitas, ad genera relatas, cum differentiis specificis, nominibus trivialibus, synonymis selectis, locis natalibus, secundum systema sexuale digestas. Editio secunda, aucta. Holmiæ, impensis direct. Laurentii Salvii, 1762-63.

2 v. 20½ cm.

Paged continuously.
Title in red and black.
Frontispiece wanted.

Book plate: Adam Smith.

83. —— *ditto* ——
Bonar, p. 101.

Date: 1768.

Caroli a Linné... Systema naturæ, per regna tria naturae, secundum classes, oridines, genera, species cum characteribus, differentiis, synonymis, locis. Editio decima tertia ad Editionem duodecimam reformatam Holmiensem. Vindobonae, typis Joannis Thomae nob. de Trattnern, 1767-70.

3 v. in 4. 3 fold. pl. 20½ cm.

Tome 1 in 2 pt., paged continuously.

Book plate: Adam Smith.

84. **Locke, John,** 1632-1704.
Bonar, p. 102.

An essay concerning human understanding. In four books. Written by John Locke, gent. The 9th edition, with large additions... London, printed by T. W. for A. Churchill; and E. Parker, 1726.

2 v. front. (port.) 20½ cm.

Book plate: Adam Smith.

Vol. ii: "Printed by M. J. for..."

Locke is very often referred to by Adam Smith.
See Bonar, pp. 102-103.

85. **Lucretius Carus, Titus.**   Bonar, p. 105.

T. Lucretii Cari, De rerum natura libri sex, cum
notis integris Dionysii Lambini, Oberti Gifanii, Tana-
quilli Fabri, Thomæ Creech, et selectis Jo. Baptistæ
Pii, aliorumque, curante Sigeberto Havercampo, qui
& suas & Abrahami Preigeri adnotationes adjecit.
Accedunt interpretatio Thomæ Creech, variae lectiones
ex notulis Is. Vossii, atque ex plus quam viginti quin-
que codd. tam impress. quam mss. ut & complures
iique locupletissimi indices. Cum figuris artificiosis-
simis atque venustissimis. Lugduni Batavorum, apud
Janssonios van der Aa, 1725.

2 v. front., vi pl. 26½ cm.

Title vignette.

Present copy is number 403 ("exemplar... qua-
dringentesimum tertium") of an edition of 820 copies.
cf. note at end of vol. 1 signed by the editor and publisher.

Vol. II without separate title-page.

Book plate: Adam Smith.

Haverkamp, Syvert, 1684-1724, ed.
Lambin Denys, 1520 or 21-1572.
Giffen, Hubert van, 1534-1604.
Lefebvre, Tannegui, 1615-1672.
Creech, Thomas, 1659-1700.
Pio, Giovanni Battista, d. 1540?
Preiger, Abraham.
Vossius, Isaac, 1618-1689.

86. **Lyttelton, George Lyttelton, *1st baron*,**   Bonar, p. 106.
    1709-1773.

The history of the life of King Henry the Second,
and of the age in which he lived, in five books: to
which is prefixed, a history of the revolutions of
England from the death of Edward the Confessor to
the birth of Henry the Second: by George, lord Lyttel-

ton... London, printed for W. Sandby and J. Dodsley, 1767.

Vol. 2 only. 29½×24½ cm.

Title vignette.
Marginal note.

Book plate: Adam Smith.

87. Machiavelli, Niccolò, 1469-1527.

Bonar, p. 106.

Opere di Niccolò Macchiavelli, coll' aggiunta delle inedite... Londra, appresso Marcello Prault, 1768.

7 v. (i.e. vol. 1, 3-8) front. (port.) plates, fold. tab., fold. plan. 14½ cm.

Engraved title-page.

Book plate: Adam Smith.

Machiavelli is referred to by Adam Smith in Mor. Sent. Pt. VI. Sect. 1. W. of N. III. 180. 1, V. i. 354. 2, and V. ii. 368. 1. See Bonar, pp. 106-107.

88. Macpherson, James, 1736-1796.

Bonar, p. 108.

Temora, an ancient epic poem, in eight books: together with several other poems, composed by Ossian, the son of Fingal. Translated from Galic language, by J. Macpherson. London, printed for T. Becket and P. A. De Hondt, 1763.

2 p.l., xxxiv, [2] 247, [5] 75, [1]p. 26×21 cm.

Title in red and black, title vignette.

"A critical dissertation on the poems of Ossian, the son of Fingal." with special title-page, and pagination.

Book plate: Adam Smith.

89. Major, John, 1460-1550.

Bonar, p. 110.

Historia Maioris Britanniæ, tam Angliæ q̄ Scotiæ, per Ioannem Maiorem, nomine quidem Scotum, professione autem theologum, e veterum monumentis concinnata. [Paris] Vænundatur Iodoco Badio Ascensio [1521].

10 p.l., folio 1-146. 20½ cm.

Collophon on last page: Ex officina Ascenciana, 1521.
Printer's device, printing press, on title-page.
Running title: De gestis Scotorum, lib. I-[vi].
Engraved initials.

Book plate: Adam Smith.

90. Malpighi, Marcello, 1628-1694.

Marcelli Malpighii Philosophi & Medici Bononiensis... Opera omnia, figuris elegantissimis in æs incisis illustrata. Tomis duobus comprehensa. Quorum catalogum sequens pagina exhibet. Londini, apud Robertum Scott & Georgium Wells, 1686.

2 v. front. (vol. 1), plates (part. fold.) 37½ cm.

Title in red and black.
Each article has special pagination.

Book plate: Adam Smith.
Ms. on title-page: J. Amson, M.

Contents:
Vol. 1. Plantarum Anatomes partem primam.—Epistolas varias ad Oldenburgium & Sponium.
Vol. 2. Plantarum Anatomes partem secundam.—Dissertat. Epistolicas. I. De Bombyce. II. De formatione Pulli in Ovo.—Exercitationes Epistolicas. I. De Cerebro. II. De Lingua. III. De externo Tactûs Organs. IV. De Omento, Pinguedine & Adiposis Ductibus.—Exercitatio. Anatomica de Viscerum Structura.—Dissertationes de Polypo Cordis, & de Pulmanibus. &c.

91. —— ditto ——

Marcelli Malpighii Philosophi & Medici Bononiensis... Opera posthuma, figuris æneis illustrata. Quibus præfixa est ejusdem vita à seipso scripta.

Bonar, p. 111.

No. of vols.: 3

Bonar,
No entry.

Londini, impensis A. & F. Churchill, 1697.

1 p.l., 110, 187, [3] 10 p. front., port., plates 37½ cm.

Title in red and black, vignette.

Book plate: Adam Smith.

Ms. on title-page: J. Amson, M.

92. Maundrell, Henry, 1665-1701.
Bonar, p. 112.

A journey from Aleppo to Jerusalem at Easter, A.D. 1697. The 2nd edition, in which the corrections and additions, which were sent by the author after the book was printed off, are inserted in the body of the book in their proper places. By Hen. Maundrell ... Oxford, printed at the Theater, 1707.

6 p.l., 145, 7 p. 9 pl. (5 fold.) 20 cm.

Title vignette.

Book plate: Stuart of Dunnairn, Esq.; Adam Smith.

Ms. note on fly-leaf: Rob: Holte.

93. Millar, John, 1735-1801.
Bonar, p. 115.

Observations concerning the distinction of ranks in society. By John Millar, Esq... London, printed by W. & J. Richardson, for J. Murray, 1771.

2 p.l., xvii, 242 p., 1 1. 27½×21½ cm.

Half title.

Book plate: Adam Smith.

Adam Smith sent his cousin David Douglas to study law at Glasgow under the care of John Millar, Professor of Laws at Glasgow University. See Bonar, p. 115.

94. Milton, John, 1608-1674.
Bonar, p. 116,

Paradise regain'd. A poem, in four books. To which is added Samson Agonistes; and Poems upon several occasions, with a Tractate of education. The author John Milton. The eighth edition. London, printed for J. and R. Tonson [etc., etc.] 1743.

3 p.l., 352 p. front. 17 cm.

Head and tail pieces.

"Samson agonistes" and "Poems upon several occasions" have each special title-page.

Book plate: Adam Smith.

95. **Molière, Jean Baptiste Poquelin,** 1622-1673.

Œuvres de Molière. Nouvelle édition... A Paris, Chez Damonneville, 1749.

Vol. 8 only. plates 14½ cm.

Title vignette, in red and black.

Book plate: Adam Smith.

Tome 8 contains: La comtesse d'Escarbagnas. Le malade imaginaire. Remerciment au roi. La gloire du Val-de-grâce. Extraits de divers auteurs. Recueil de plusieurs pièces en vers.

Bonar, p. 118.
Date: 1725.

96. **Mulgrave, Constantine John Phipps,** *2d baron,* 1744-1792.

A voyage towards the North pole undertaken by his Majesty's command, 1773. By Constantine John Phipps. London, printed by W. Bowyer & J. Nicholas, for J. Nourse, 1774.

viii, 253 p., 1 l. incl. fold. tables. front., fold. plates, fold. maps, fold. plan. 29 cm.

Book plate: Adam Smith.

Bonar, p. 141.
Heading:
Phipps (C. J.)

97. **Nicolson, William,** *abp. of Cashel,* 1655-1727.

The Irish historical library. Pointing at most of the authors and records in print or manuscript, which may be serviceable to the compilers of a general history of Ireland. By William, lord bishop of Derry...

Bonar, p. 197.
Heading:
William.
[Not listed as J.]

Dublin, printed by A. Rhames, for W. Taylor, 1724.

xxxviii p., 1 1., 246, [10]p. 19¾ cm.

Book plate: Adam Smith.

Appendix II is a translation of the Irish preface, to Mr. Lhuyd's Irish dictionary.
Appendix III is a translation of the Welsh preface, to Mr. Lhuyd's Glossography.

Lhuyd, Edward, 1660-1709.

William Nicolson, successively Bp. of Carlisle, and of Derry, and Abp. of Cashel.

98. [**Orme, Robert**] 1728-1801.

A history of the military transactions of the British nation in Indostan, from the year 1745, to which is prefixed a dissertation on the establishments made by Mahomedan conquerors in Indostan... the 2nd edition, corrected, with alteration, additions, and an index, by the author. London, printed for J. Nourse, 1775-78.

2 v. fold. maps, fold. plans. 27½×22 cm.

Published anonymously.

Book plate: Adam Smith.

Bonar, p. 83.

Heading:
Hindostan.

Bonar, p. 124.

Date: 1775.
[Not listed as J.]

99. **Parnaso italiano ovvero,** raccolta de' poeti classici italiani d'ogni genere, d'ogni età d'ogni metro e del più scelto tra gli ottimi, diligentemente riveduti sugli originali più accreditati, e adornati di figure in rame. Venezia, presso A. Zatta e figli, 1784-88.

Bonar, p. 138.

32 v. 15½ cm.

Half-title; each volume has also special title-page. Title vignette (port.); head-pieces.
Edited by Andrea Rubbi.

Book plate: Adam Smith.

Contents:—Vols. 1-2. Francesco Petrarca. 1784. — Vols. 3-5. Dante Alighieri. 1784. —Vol. 6. Lirici anti-

chi serj e giocosi fino al secolo xvi. 1784. —Vols. 7-9.
Morgante Maggiore di messer Luigi Pulci. 1784. —Vol.
10. Poemetti del secolo xv. xvi. 1785. —Vols. 11-15.
Orlando innamorato di Matteo Ma. Bojardo, rifatto da
Francesco Berni. 1785. —Vol. 16. Egloghe boscherecce
del secolo xv. xvi. 1785. —Vol. 17. Teatro autico;
tragico, comico, pastorale, drammatico. 1785. —Vols.
18-22. Orlando furioso di M. Lodovico Ariosto. 1785. —
Vol. 23. Alamanni, Ruccellai, Tansillo, Baldi, didas-
calici del secolo xvi. 1786. —Vol. 24. [Torquato Tasso]
Aminta, [A. Ongaro] Alceo, [G. B. G. Cinthio] Egle,
favole teatrali del secolo xvi. 1786. —Vol. 25. Baldi,
Rota, Franco, Del Vasto, Fidentio, Marittimi e pedan-
teschi del secolo xvi. 1787. —Vol. 26. Ariosto, Casti-
glione, Fracastoro, Sanazzaro, Casa, canzonieri del
secolo xvi. 1787. —Vol. 27. Ariosto, Berni, satirici e
burleschi del secolo xvi. 1787. —Vols. 28-29. Geru-
salemme liberata di Torquato Tasso. 1787. —Vol. 30.
Costanzo, Torquato Tasso, Bernardo Tasso, e poetesse
del secolo xvi. 1787. —Vol. 31. Lirici misti del secolo
xvi. 1787. —Vol. 32. Lirici Veneziani del secolo xvi.
1788.

100. [**Pennant, Thomas**] 1726-1798.   Bonar, p. 140.

British zoology... London, printed for B. White;
Chester, printed by E. Adams for B. White, 1768-70.

4 v. plates (part. fold.) 22½ cm.

Vol. 1 and 2 paged continuously.
Dedication signed by the author.
Each volume has special title-page only.
Title-page of Vol. 1: British zoology. Class I.
Quadrupeds. Class II. Birds. London, printed for B.
White, 1768. —Vol. 2: British zoology. Class II.
Genus XVIII, etc. Birds. With an appendix, an essay
on birds of passage, and an index. London, printed for
B. White, 1768. —Vol. 3: British zoology. Class III.
Reptiles. Class IV. Fish. Chester, printed by E. Adams,

for B. White, 1769. —Vol. 4: British zoology. Illustrated by plates and brief explanations. Chester, printed by E. Adams, 1770.

Book plate: Adam Smith.

101.   —— [*ditto*] ——

Bonar, p. 140.

A tour in Scotland; 1769... The 3rd edition. Warrington, printed by W. Eyres, 1774.

No. of vols. :
3 vols.

xiv, 388, 1 p. illus., xxi pl. (incl. ports., part. fold.) 23½×19½ cm.

Title vignette, marginal notes.

Dedication signed by the author.

Book plate: Adam Smith.

Appendix no. I. Of Scotch pines, by J. Farquharson. II. Of Elgin and the shire of Murray, by the rev. Mr. Shaw. III. The life of James Crichton, of Clunie; commonly called the Admirable Crichton.   IV. Of the murder of a Laird of Innes, as related in the old account. V. Of Cathness, Strathnaver, and Sutherland, by the rev. Mr. A. Pope. VI. The life of Sir Ewen Cameron, of Lochiel. VII. Of the massacre of the Colquhouns. VIII. Itinerary.

102.   —— [*ditto*] ——

Bonar,
No entry.

A tour in Scotland, and Voyage to the Hebrides; 1772. Chester, printed by J. Monk; London, printed for B. White, 1774-76.

2 v. lxxxviii pl. (incl. ports., maps, part. fold.) 24×19½ cm.

Title vignette, with marginal notes.

Dedication signed by the author.

Book plate: Adam Smith.

Vol. 1 is called the Second tour, Vol. 2 the Third tour in Scotland.
Vol. 1, Chester, printed by J. Monk, 1774.

Vol. 2, London, printed for B. White, 1776.

103. **Percy, Thomas, bp. of Dromore,** 1729-1811.

Bonar, p. 140.

Reliques of ancient English poetry: consisting of old heroic ballads, songs and other pieces of our earlier poets, (chiefly of the lyric kind.), together with some few of later date. The 2nd edition... London, printed for J. Dodsley, 1767.

Vol. 1 only. front. 17½ cm.

Title vignette, head and tail pieces.

Book plate: Adam Smith.

2nd ed. published in 3 vols.

104. **[Philosophical Society of Edinburgh]**

Bonar, p. 66.

Heading:
Essays.

Essays and observations, physical and literary. Read before a society in Edinburgh, and published by them. Edinburgh, printed by G. Hamilton & J. Balfour, 1756.

Vol. 2 only. 7 fold. pl. 20 cm.

Book plate: Adam Smith.

3 vols published during 1754-71, are the second series of Essays published by the society.

Contents:—I. The description of a new plant; by Dr. Alex Garden. II. A description of the matrix or ovary of the Buccinum Ampullatum; by Robert Whytt. etc., etc.

105. **Pinkerton, John,** 1738-1826.

Bonar, . 141.

An enquiry into the history of Scotland, preceding the reign of Malcom III., or the year 1056. Including the authentic history of that period... By John Pinkerton... London, printed by J. Nicholas, for G. Nicol [etc., etc.] 1789.

2 v. front., fold. maps, fold. geneal. tables. 20½cm.

Bibliography: vol. 1, pp. lxx-lxxviii.

"A dissertation on the origin and progress of the

Scythians, or Goths," London, 1787 (with special title-page and separate paging): vol. 2, xxii, 207, [2]p.

Book plate: Adam Smith.

106. **Rabelais, François, 1490-1553?**

Bonar, p. 154.

Œuvres de maître François Rabelais, avec des remarques historiques et critiques de M. Le Duchat. Nouvelle édition, ornée de figures de B. Picart &c. augmentée de quantité de nouvelles remarques de M. le Duchat, de celles de l'édition angloise des œuvres de Rabelais, de ses lettres, & de plusieurs pièces curieuses & intéressantes... A Amsterdam, Chez J. F. Bernard, 1741.

3 v. illus., pl. (incl. port., part. fold.) fold. map. 25 cm.

Added title-page engraved.
Title vignette, head and tail pieces.
Book plate: Adam Smith.

"Remarques sur les œuvres de maître François Rabelais, publiées en anglois par Mr. le Motteux, et traduites en françois par C.D.M." vol. 3; with separate page.

"La Vie de François Rabelais." vol. 3.

Le Duchat, Jacob, 1658-1735, ed.
Motteux, Peter Anthony, 1663-1718.

107. **Rapin, René, 1621-1687.**

Bonar, p. 155.

Heading :
Rapin (Paul de Thoyras).
[1661-1725]

Les œuvres diverses du P. Rapin. Qui contiennent. L'Esprit du christianisme. La Perfection du christianisme, L'Importances du salut. La Foy des derniers siecles... A Amsterdam, Chez P. Mortier, 1695.

6 p.l., 107, [13], 369, [2]p. 16½ cm.

Title in red and black. Title vignette, head and tail pieces.

Book plate: Adam Smith.

108. **Respublica,** sive status regni Scotiæ et Hiberniæ. Diversorum autorum. Lugd. Bat., ex officina Elzeviriana, 1627.

Bonar, p. 164.

Heading:
Scotland.

282, [2]p. 11×5½ cm.

Engraved title-page.

Colophon on last page: Lvgd. Bat., ex officinâ Elzeviriana, anno 1630.

Selections from Buchanan, Camden, Boethius, etc.

109. **Robertson, William,** 1721-1793.

Bonar, p. 158.

The history of America. By William Robertson ... The 2nd edition. London, printed for W. Strahan & T. Cadell [etc.] 1778.

2 v. fold. plates, 4 fold. maps (incl. fronts.) 27×22 cm.

"A catalogue of Spanish books and manuscripts": vol. 2, pp. [519]-535.

Book plate: Adam Smith.

110. —— *ditto* ——

Bonar, p. 158.

The history of the reign of the Emperor Charles V., by William Robertson... London, printed by W. and W. Strahan for W. Strahan [etc.] 1769.

3 v. 28 cm.

Vol. 1 has title: The history of the reign of Emperor Charles V., with a view of the progress of society in Europe, from the subversion of the Roman empire to the beginning of the sixteenth century...
Vol. 3 includes index to vols. 2-3.

Book plate: Adam Smith.

111. **Rousseau, Jean Jacques,** 1712-1778.

Bonar, p. 160.

Émile, ou De l'éducation. Par J. J. Rousseau, citoyen de Genève. A Francfort, 1762.

Vol. 3 only. 17½ cm.

Title in red and black.

Book plate: Adam Smith.

*On the references by Adam Smith to Rousseau,
see* Bonar, pp. 160-161.

112. **Ruchat, Abraham,** 1678-1750.

Bonar, p. 161.

Histoire de la réformation de la Suisse, où l'on voit
tout ce qui s'est passé de plus remarquable, depuis l'an
1516. jusqu'en l'an 1556., dans les églises des XIII. Can-
tons, & des Etats confédérés, qui composent avec eux
le L. corps helvétique. Par Abraham Ruchat,...
Professeur en belle lettres dans l'Académie de Lausanne.
A Geneve, Chez M. M. Bousquet et comp., 1727-28.

6 v. front. (vol. 1) 16½ cm.

Title in red and black, title vignette.

Book plate: Adam Smith.

On the references by Adam Smith to Ruchat, see
Bonar, p. 161.

113. **Russia seu Moscovia** itemque Tartaria commen-
tario topographico atque politico illustratæ. Lugd.
Batavorum, ex officina Elzeviriana, 1630.

Bonar, p. 161.

Heading:
Russia.

4 p.l., 345, [19]p. 11½×5½ cm.

Engraved title-page.

With this is bound "Respublica Moscoviæ et
urbes... 1630" by M. Z. Boxhorn.

114. **Russia seu Moscovia** itemque Tartaria commen-
tario topographico atque politico illustratæ. Lugd.
Batavorum, ex officina Elzeviriana, 1630.

Bonar, p. 161.

*No double en-
try.*

327, [7]p. 11 cm.

Engraved title-page.

Bound with "Turcici imperii status... 1634".

There are two copies of "Russia seu Moscovia..."
in Adam Smith's library; one is bound with "Respu-
blica Moscoviæ et urbes...", and the other is bound
with "Turcici imperii status..."

115. Salmon, Thomas, 1679-1767.

Bonar, p. 163.

A short view of the families of the present Irish
nobility; their marriages, issue, descents, and immediate
ancestors; the posts of honour and profit they hold in
the government; their arms, mottos, and chief seats.
With an index, specifying the time of their respective
creations, and summons to parliament; the titles of
their eldest sons; their rank, precedence, &c. By Mr.
Salmon. London, printed for W. Owen, 1759.

Title:
A short view of the peerage of Ireland.

3 p.l., 272, [7]p. 17½ cm.

Book plate: Adam Smith.

116. Sandys, George, 1578-1644.

Bonar, p. 164.

Sandys Travels, containing an history of the original and present state of the Turkish empire... the
Mahometan religion and ceremonies: a description of
Constantinople... also of Greece... Of Egypt... A
description of the Holy-Land... Lastly, Italy described,
and the islands adjoining... Illustrated with fifty
graven maps and figures. The 7th edition. London,
printed for J. Williams junior, 1673.

2 p.l., 240 p. illus. (incl. plans and maps) fold.
pl. 32½ cm.

Head and tail pieces, initials, marginal notes.
Engraved added title-page wanted?

Book plate: Adam Smith; Stuart of Dunnairn Esq.

Ms. on title-page and p. 1: John Williams...

117. Sarpi, Paolo, 1552-1623.

Bonar, p. 130.

Opere del padre Paolo dell' ordine de' Servi; e
theologo della serenissima repvblica di Venetia... In

Heading:
Paolo (Padre, Sarpi).
Date: 1688.

Venetia, appresso Roberto Meietti, 1681-1694.

6 v. front. (port., vol. 1) 14½ cm.

Each work has special title-page, and paged separately.

The title-pages are dated 1681-1694, irregularly. Vol. 1 has general title-page; vols. 2-6 collective half-title only.

Book plate: Adam Smith.

Contents:—Vol. 1. Vita del padre Paolo [da Fulgenio Micanxio]... 1694. Trattato dell' interdetto della santità di papa Paolo V. composto da frà Paolo, dell' ordine de' Servi. Ed altri theologhi di sotto nominati. Pietr' Antonio... f. Bernardo Giordano... f. Michael Agnolo... f. Marc' Antonio Capello... f. Camillo... f. Fvlgentio... 1687. Theologorvm venetorum Joan. Marsillii, Pauli Veneti, fr. Fulgentii, ad excommunicationis, citationis, & monitionis romanæ, sententiam in ipsos latam responsio... 1686.

Vol. 2. Considerationi sopra le censure della santità di papa Paolo V. contra la serenissima republica di Venetia... 1686. Trattato e resolutione sopra la validità delle scommuniche, di Gio. Gersone... tr. dalla lingua latina... In opusculi due... 1687. Apologia per l'oppositioni fatte dall' illustrissimo & reverendissimo signor cardinale Bellarmino. Alli trattati, & risolutioni di Gio. Gersone, sopra la validità delle scommuniche... 1687.

Vol. 3. Historia dell' origine, forma, leggi, ed uso dell' ufficio dell' inquisizione nella città, e dominio di Venetia... 1687. Trattato delle materie beneficiarie di frà Paolo Sarpi, nel quale si narra, col fondamento dell' historie, come si dispensassero l'elemosine de' fedeli nella primitiva chiesa. In Mirandola, 1683. De jure asylorum liber singularis Petri Sarpi I.C. aliàs patris Pauli Servitæ. Accesserunt viri eruditi de asylis collectanea de italien in latinam linguam tr. ab A. Frikelburgio 1683.

Vol. 4. Historia particolare delle cose passate trà il sommo pontefice Paolo V. e la serenissima republica di Venetia... In Mirandola, 1687.

Vol. 5. Historia degli Uscochi scritta da Minucio Minuci... sino all' anno M.DC.II. e continuata dal p.m. Paolo... sino all' anno M.DC.XVI... 1683.

Vol. 6. Domino del mar Adriatico della serenissima republica di Venetia... 1686. Dominio del mar' Adriatico, e sue raggioni per il ius belli della serenissima republica di Venetia... 1685. Allegatione in iure contro l'autor degl' annali ecclesiastici [Cesare Baroulo] Qual nel suo duodecimo tomo niega la verità della vittoria navale ottenuta dalla serenissima republica di Venetia. Contro Federico I. imperatore, e l'atto di papa Allessandro III. Composta dall' eccellentissimo. Cornelio Frangipani... 1685. Opinione del padre Paolo Servita... come debba governarsi internamente, ed esternamente la serenissima Republica di Venetia, per havere il perpetuo dominio... Per publica commissione... 1681.

118. Saxe, Maurice, comte de, 1696-1750.

Bonar, p. 32.

Heading: Bonneville.

Les rêveries, ou Mémoires sur l'art de la guerre de Maurice comte de Saxe, duc de Courlande et de Semigalle Marechal-General des armées... dediés à messieurs les officiers généraux, par Mr. de Bonneville, capitaine ingénieur de campagne de Sa Majesté le Roi de Prusse. A La Haye, Chez P. Gosse junior, 1758.

xii, 228 p., 2 l., xl pl., 15 p. plates (part. fold.) 37 cm.

Title vignette; head and tail pieces.

"Réflexions sur la propagation de l'espèce humaine": pp. 219-228.

Book plate: Adam Smith.

Contents:

Bk. 1. ch. i. De la manière de lever les Troupes,

de celle de les habiller, de les entretenir, de les païer, de les exercer & de les former pour le combat. —ch. ii. De la légion. —ch. iii. De la cavalerie; de ses armures & de ses armes, etc. —ch. iv. Dissertation sur la grande manœuvre. De la colonne. —ch. v. Des armes à feu & de la méthode de tirer. —ch. vi. Des drapeaux ou enseignes. —ch. vii. De l'artillerie & du Charoir. —ch. viii. De la discipline militaire.

Bk. 2. ch. i. De la fortification, attaque & défense des places. —ch. ii. Réflexions sur la guerre en général, etc. —ch. iii. De la guerre des montagnes. —ch. iv. Des païs coupés remplis de hayes & de fossés. —ch. v. Des passages de rivières. —ch. vi. Des différentes situations pour camper les armées & pour combattre. —ch. vii. Des retranchemens & des lignes. —ch. viii. De l'attaque des retranchemens. —ch. ix. Des redoutes & de leurs excellences dans les ordres de bataille. —ch. x. Des espions & de guides. —ch. xi. Des indices. —ch. xii. Des qualités que doit avoir un général d'armée.

119. **Scaliger, Julius Caesar,** 1484-1558.

Bonar, p. 164

Date: 1559.

Ivlii Caesaris Scaligeri... Poetices libri septem: I, Historicus, II, Hyle, III, Idea, IIII, Parasceue, V, Criticus, VI, Hypercriticus, VII, Epinomis, ad sylvium filium... [Lyon] apud Antonium Vincentium, 1561.

6 p.l., 364, [36] 54 (i.e. 42) p. 30 cm.

Printer's device, initials, marginal notes.

"Jullii Cæsaris Scaligeri... In librum de insomnijs Hippocratis commentarius auctus nunc & recognitus... 1561?" imprints pressed without ink; page nos. 21-42 paged 33-54.

Book plate: Adam Smith.

Front and back board of cover tooled crown and arms "Brabant".

120. **Sleidanus, Johannes,** 1506-1556.

I. Sleidani De quatuor summis imperiis libri tres: Postrema editione hac accurate recogniti. Amstelodami, apud Ludovicum Elzevirium, 1654.

309, [24]p. 10½×5½ cm.

Engraved title-page.
Running title: De monarchiis liber I [-iii].

Bonar. p. 168.

Heading: Sleidan (Johann).

121. **Smith, Adam,** 1723-1790.

A catalogue of books belonging to Adam Smith Esqr... 1781.

87 l., with 3 blank l. 38¼ cm.

Ms. copy hand-written.
Water-mark of the paper used are Crown and Fleur-de-lis with letters LVG and JW.

The full contents of this catalogue are reproduced in Appendix II. Bonar's entry; Date: 1761 is not right, due to the error of Kawai's list. cf. Scott, W. R., Adam Smith as Student and Professor, 1937, p. 172.

Bonar. p. 174.

Date: 1761.

122. —— *ditto* ——

An inquiry into the nature and causes of the wealth of nations. By Adam Smith, LL.D. and F. R.S. of London and Edinburgh: one of the commissioners of His Majesty's customs in Scotland; and formerly Professor of Moral Philosophy in the University of Glasgow. The 4th edition. London, printed for A. Strahan and T. Cadell, 1786.

3 v. tables. 22 cm.

*Bonar,
No entry.*

123. —— *ditto* ——

The theory of moral sentiments; or, An essay towards an analysis of the principles by which men naturally judge concerning the conduct and character,

Bonar. p. 170.

first of their neighbours, and afterwards of themselves. To which is added, A dissertation on the origin of languages. By Adam Smith, LL.D. Fellow of the royal societies of London and Edinburgh; one of the commissioners of His Majesty's customs in Scotland; and formerly professor of moral philosophy in the University of Glasgow. The 6th edition, with considerable additions and corrections. London, printed for A. Strahan, T. Cadell [etc., etc.] 1790.

2 v. 21 cm.

Ms. on front pannel of vol. 1: D. Douglas.

Pannels of vol. 2 wanting.

124. —— ditto ——   Bonar, p. 171.

Theorie der moralischen Empfindungen von Adam Smith. Nach der dritten englischen Ausgabe übersetzt. Braunschweig, in der Meyerischen Buchhandlung, 1770.

1 p.l., [3]-576 p. 18 cm.

Book plate: Adam Smith.

125. —— ditto ——   Bonar, p. 173.

Untersuchung der Natur und Ursachen von Nationalreichthümern von Adam Smith, Beyder Rechte Doktor, Mitglied der Koeniglichen Gesellschaft der Wissenschaften zu London und ehemaligem Lehrer der Moral-philosophie auf der Universitaet zu Glasgow. Aus dem Englischen. Leipzig, bey Weidmanns Erben und Reich, 1776.

Vol. 1 only. 20½ cm. .

Title vignette.

Book plate: Adam Smith.

Bonar says, "The book is now rare." See Bonar, p. 173.

126. **Spallanzani, Lazzaro,** 1729-1799.

Opuscoli di fisica animale, e vegetabile dell' abate Spallanzani... Aggiuntevi alcune lettere relative ad essi opuscoli dal celebre signor Bonnet di Ginevra, e da altri scritte all' autore... In Modena, presso la Societa' tipografica, 1776.

2 v. vi fold. plates 21½ cm.

Title vignette. Initials; head-pieces.

Book plate: Adam Smith.

Contents:

Vol. 1. Opuscolo I: Osservazioni, e sperienze intorno agli animalucci delle infusioni in occasione che si esaminano alcuni articoli della nuova opera del sig. di Needham. Lettere due dissertatorie; scritte dall' illustre sig. Bonnett di Ginevra all' autore relative al suggetto degli animali infusorj.

Vol. 2. Opuscolo II: Osservazioni, e sperienze intorno al vermicelli spermatici dell' uomo, e degli animali, nelle quali si prende singolarmente ad esaminare il famoso sistema delle molecole organiche. Opuscolo III: Osservazioni, e sperienze intorno agli animali, e ai vegetabili chiusi nell' aria. Opuscolo IV: Osservazioni e sperienze intorno ad alcuni prodigiosi animali, che è in balia dell' osservatore il farli tornare da morte a vita. Opuscolo V: Osservazioni, e sperienze intorno all' origine delle piantine delle muffe.

Bonnet, Charles, 1720-1793.
Needham, John Turberville, 1713-1781.

127. **Sprecher von Bernegg, Fortunat,** 1585-1647.

F. Sprecheri Rhetia, ubi eius verus situs, politia, bella, foedera, et alia memorabilia accuratissimè describuntur. Lugd. Batavorum, ex officina Elzeviriana, 1633.

424, [7]p. 11½×6 cm.

Bonar, p. 178.

Date: 1766.

Bonar, p. 178.

Heading:
Sprechieri.
[Not listed as
J.]

Engraved title-page.

Running title: Palladis rhæticæ liber I [-x].

First published at Basel, 1617, under title: Pallas rhætica, armata et togata...

128. **Stanley, Thomas,** 1625-1678.

The history of philosophy: containing the lives, opinions, actions and discourses of the philosophers of every sect. Illustrated with the effigies of divers of them. By Thomas Stanley, Esq. The 2nd edition. London, printed for T. Bassett [etc.] 1687.

13 p.l., 1091, [1]p. front. (port.) ports. 37 cm.

Title in red and black, with marginal notes. Part XIV-XIX. "The history of the Chaldaick philosophy," pp.[1025]-1091, with special title-page.

129. **Status particularis regiminis S. C. Majestatis Ferdinandi II.** [Lugduni Batavorum, ex officina Elzeviriana] 1637.

8 p.l., 365 p. 11×6 cm.

Engraved title-page.

Imprints according to catalogue of Library of Congress; but British Museum mentions as "Amsterdam". "Daniellis Eremitæ, Belgæ, Itergermanicum. Sive epistola ad Camillum Guidium, equitem; scripta de legatione Magnæ Hetruriæ ducis ad Rudolph. II. Caesarem Augustum, & aliquot Germaniæ principes & respublicas anno MDCIX": pp. [297]-365.

L'Hermite, Daniel, 1584?-1613.

130. **[Stephanius, Stephen Hansen]** 1599-1650, *ed.*

De regno Daniæ et Norwegiæ, Insulisque adjacentibus: juxtà ac de Holsatia, Dvcatv sleswicensi, et finitimis provincijs, tractatus varij. Lvgdvni Batavorvm, ex officina Elzeviriana, 1629.

8 p.l., 447, [5]p., 1 l. 11½×5½ cm.

Bonar, p. 178. [Not listed as J.]

Bonar, p. 69. *Heading:* Fernandus II.

Bonar, p. 56. *Heading:* Denmark.

Printer's device on title-page.

Title within border, arms of Danish provinces.

Dedication signed: Stephanus Iohannis Stephanius.

"Arngrimi Ionae Islandi tractatus de islandicæ gentis primordiis, & veteri republica": pp. 299-437.

Ms. on fly-leaf.

Contents:—I. Magistri Adami canonici bremensis Libellus de situ Daniæ... —II. Chronographica Daniæ descriptio, compendio è Jona Coldingensi & Isacio Pontano, alliisque excerpta. —III. Coeli solique qualitates & regni Daniæ dotes. —IV. Mores, ingenia & instituta Daniæ gentis. —V. Regni danici status politicus. —VI. Erici Daniæ regis... Historica narratio de origine gentis Danorum... —VII. Historia compendiosa ac succincta... Daniæ regum, ab incerto auctore descripta... & antehac in lucem edita operâ & studio Erpoldi Lindenbruch. —VIII. Excerpta libelli Jonæ ab Elvervelt, de Holsatia... —IX. Angrimi Jonæ Islandi tractatus de islandicæ gentis primordiis & veteri republica... Epigrammata quædam Willichii Westhovii ... de urbibus & oppidis Sælandiæ.

Vidalin, Arngrimur Jonsson, 1568-1648.

131. Strada, Jacobus de, a Rosberg, d.1588.

Bonar, p. 181.

Epitome thesauri antiquitatum, hoc est, impp. Rom. orientalium & occidentalium iconum, ex antiquis numismatibus quàm fidelissimè deliniatarum. Ex Musæo Iacobi de Strada Mantuani Antiquarij. Lugduni, Apud I. de Strada, et T. Guerinum, 1553.

44 p.l., 339, [2]p. illus. 23½ cm.

Book plate: Adam Smith.

132. Tasso, Torquato, 1544-1595.

Bonar, p. 183.

No. of vols:
4 vols.

La Gierusalemme liberata di Torquato Tasso: con le figure di Bernardo Castelli, e le annotationi di Scipio Gentili e di Giulio Guastavini. Aggiuntovi la vita dell' autore scritta da Gio. Battista Manso... Con altre aggiunte e correttioni. In Londra, appresso G. Tonson & G. Watts, 1724.

2 v. front. (port.) xx pl. 29½ cm.

Title vignette, head and tail pieces, initials.

Book plate: Adam Smith.

Annotators:
Gentili, Scipione, 1563-1616.
Guastavini, Giulio, 16th cent.

133. ── *ditto* ──   Bonar, p. 183.

La Gierusalemme liberata di Torquato Tasso: con le figure di Sebastiano Clerc... In Glasgua, della stampa di Roberto ed Andrea Foulis [etc.] 1763.

2 v. front. (port.) xx pl. 16 cm.

Added title-page engraved.

Book plate: Adam Smith.

134. **Tassoni, Alessandro,** 1565-1635.   Bonar, p. 184.

De' Pensieri diversi di Alessandro Tassoni. Libri dieci. Corretti, ampliati, e arricchiti in questa ultima impressione per tutto dall' auttore di nuoue curiosità. Ne' quali per via di quesiti con nuoui fondamenti, e ragioni si trattano le più curiose materie naturali, morali, ciuili, poetiche, istoriche, e d'altre facoltà, che soglion venire in discorso fra cauallieri, e professori di lettere. Con la tauola de' libri, quesiti, e capitoli, la qual è diligentemente reuista. In Venetia, per Domenico Miloco, 1676.

4 p.l., 361, [3]p. 21½ cm.

Half-title, initials, head and tail pieces.
Printer's device on title-page.
Book plate: Adam Smith.

Ms. notes on p. 347.

135. **Turcici imperii status.** Accedit de regn. Algeriano atque Tunetano commentarius. Lugduni Batav., ex officina Elzeviriana, 1634.

Bonar, p. 188.
Heading:
Turkey.

 4 p.l., 363, [5]p. 11 cm.

 Engraved title-page.
 With this is bound "Russia seu Moscovia itemque Tartaria... 1630."

 Ms. on title-page and fly-leaf.

136. **Tyrrell, James,** 1642-1718.

Bonar, p. 189.

 The general history of England, both ecclesiastical and civil... By James Tyrrell, esq. London, printed for W. Rogers [etc.] 1700-04.

 3 v. in 5. geneal. tables. 33 cm.

 With marginal notes.
 Title-page and front. of vol. 1 wanting, vols. 2-3 (each in 2 parts) have special title-page only.

 Book plate: Adam Smith, on another's.

 Contents:—Vol. 1. Bk. I. From the earliest accounts of time, to the First coming of Julius Cæsar. Bk. II. Containing the annals of England, from the first Landing of Julius Cæsar, to the Romans total desertion thereof, being about four hundred and ninety years. Bk. III. From its desertion by the Romans, to the preaching of christianity by Augustine the Monk, being one hundred sixty two years. Bk. IV. From the preaching of the christian religion by Augustine the Monk, to Ecbert, the first chief or supreme King of England; containing two hundred and three years. Bk. V. From the beginning of the Reign of King Egbert, to that of King Edgar; being the space of one hundred fifty six years and an half. Bk. VI. Containing the general history of England from the Reign of King Edgar, to the death of King Harold; being one hundred and seventeen years.

Vol. 2. [Part 1.] Bk. I. The Reign of King William I. commonly called the conqueror. Bk. II. King William II. Bk. III. King Henry I. Bk. IV. King Stephen. Bk. V. Containing the Reign of King Henry II. Bk. VI. Containing the Reign of King Richard I. —Vol. 2, Part 2. Bk. VII. Containing the Reign of King John. Bk. VIII. Containing the Reign of K. Henry III.

Vol. 3. [Part 1.] Bk. IX. King Edward I. Bk. X. Containing the Reign of King Edward II. Bk. XI. Containing the Reign of King Edward III. —Vol. 3, Part 2. Bk. XII. Containing the Reign of King Richard II.

Closes with the reign of Richard II.; no more published. The last volume includes (as appendix) a dissertation on representation in the House of Commons.

Reference to Tyrrell in W. of N., see Bonar, p. 189.

137. Varchi, Benedetto, 1503-1565.

Bonar, p. 190.

Storia fiorentina di Messer Benedetto Varchi. Nella quale principalmente si contengono l'ultime revoluzioni della Republica fiorentina, e lo stabilimento del principato nella casa de' Medici. Colla tavola in fine delle cose più notabili. In Colonia, Appresso P. Martello, 1721.

15 p.l., 677, [1]p., [1]l. port., double geneal. tab. 33 cm.

Engraved half-title and title vignette (medal with author's portrait). Initials, head and tail pieces.

"Vita di Messer Benedetto Varchi, scritta dall' abate Don Silvano Razzi": 4-9 prelim. leaves.

Book plate: Adam Smith.

Razzi, Girolamo, in religion Silvano, fl 1560.

138. Vasari, Giorgio, 1512-1574.

Bonar, p. 190.

Date: 1674.

Le vite de' più eccellenti pittori, scultori et architetti. Di Giorgio Vasari... In questa nuova edizione diligentemente riuiste, ricorrette, accresciute d'alcuni ritratti, & arricchite di postille nel margine. Al Serenissimo Ferdinando II. Grand Duca di Toscana. In Bologna, Presso gli heredi di Euangelista Dozza, 1647.

3 v. illus. (ports.) 24 cm.

Pt. 1 and 2 in 1 v.; pt. 3 in 2 v.

Title-page of 2 v. of pt. 3 reads: Delle vitte de' più eccellenti pittori...

Added title-page of vol. 1 engraved.

Initials, marginal notes.

Book plate: Adam Smith.

Paper with ms. inserted vol. 1, pp. 64-65.

139. **Veneroni, Giovanni,** 1642-1708.   Bonar, p. 190

Le maître italien, dans sa dernière perfection, revue, corrigé & augmenté par l'auteur; contenant tout ce qui est nécessaire pour apprendre facilement & en peu de tems la langue italienne. Avec un abregé de la prononciation françoise pour les étrangers, un dictionaire pour les deux langues, & quelques lettres è la fin. Par le sieur de Veneroni... Nouvelle édition exactement corrigée & augmentée... A Amsterdam, Chez H. du Sauzet, 1740.

4 p.l., 645 p. 16 cm.

Title in red and black, head and tail pieces.

Book plate: Adam Smith.

140. **Vitruvius Pollio.**   Bonar, p. 192.

L'architettura di M. Vitruvio Pollione, colla traduzione italiana e comento del marchese Berardo Galiani ... In Napoli, nella Stamperia Simoniana, 1758.

3 p.l., xxxii, 462 p., 26 1. front., xxv pl. (incl. plans) 40 cm.

Title vignette, initials, head and tail pieces.

Book plate: Adam Smith.

Galiani, Berardo, marchese, d. 1771, tr.

141. [**Whitelocke, Sir Bulstrode**] 1605-1675.

Memorials of the English affairs: or, An historical account of what passed from the beginning of the reign of King Charles the First, to King Charles the Second his happy restauration. Containing the publick transactions, civil and military. Together with the private consultation and secrets of the cabinet... London, printed for N. Ponder, 1682.

4 p.l., 704, 15 p. 38 cm.

With marginal notes.
Published anonymously.

Book plate: Adam Smith.
Ms. note on fly-leaf: D 37. J

"Published by Arthur, earl of Angleses, who took considerable liberties with the ms."—Lowndes, Bibliographer's manual.

APPENDIX I

Books which have been transmitted to us as a portion of the Library of Adam Smith, but really published after his death.

Henry, Robert, 1718-1790.

The history of Great Britain, from the first invasion of it by the Romans under Julius Caesar. Written on a new plan. By Robert Henry... London, printed for A. Strahan & T. Cadell, 1793.

Vol. 6 only. 27 cm.

"The life of Robert Henry" vii-xx.
Dedication signed by H. Moncreiff Wellwood, Wm. Balderstone, and Wm. Finlay.

1st ed. published in 6 vols. during 1771-93.

Ms. on inside of front board: David Douglas.

Vol. 6 was published after Adam Smith's death, so this book ought to be excluded from the entry. cf. Bonar, p. 82.

Smith, Adam, 1723-1790.

Essays on philosophical subjects. By the late Adam Smith, LL.D. Fellow of the royal societies of London and Edinburgh, &c., &c. To which is prefixed, an account of the life and writings of the author; by Dugald Stewart, F.R.S.E ... London, printed for T. Cadell, jun., & W. Davies [etc.] 1795.

xcv, 244 p. 28×22 cm.

Edited by Joseph Black & James Hutton.

Ms. on front pannel: David Douglas.

Stewart, Dugald, 1753-1828.
Black, Joseph, 1728-1799, ed.
Hutton, James, 1726-1797, ed.

This book was published after Adam Smith's death, so it ought not to be included in this catalogue. cf. Bonar, p. 214.

APPENDIX II

A Catalogue of books belonging to Adam Smith, Esqr. 1781. A handwriting manuscript of 87 sheets, together with 3 blank sheets. Originally drawn up by or for Adam Smith himself.

A

Catalgue of Books,
[*sic*]

Belonging to

Adam Smith Esq.

1781

A Catalogue of Books

FIRST DIVISION

Upper Row

Gibbon's History of the decline & fall of the Roman Empire.
Vol. 1, 2, 3

ᴦ. 1   Choix des Memoires de L'academie Royal des Inscriptions et
Belles-Lettres 3 Toms.

La Republique Romaine ou Plan General de L'ancien Gouvernement de Rome 2 Toms.

ᴦ. 82   Henry's Hist. of G. Britain written on a New Plan   Vols
1, 2, 3

ᴦ. 106 Lytteltons Hist. of the life of King Henry the second & of

Bonar

the age in which he lived.   3 Vols, With a Vol of Notes to the Second & Third books of his life.

†Macphersons Critical Dissertation on the Origin Antiquities, Language &c⁸, of the ancient Caledonians.

†An Introduction to the Hist: of G: Britain and Ireland by Ja⁸ M..cpherson.

p. 108   ——— History of G. B. from the Revolution to the accession of the House of Hanover 2 Vols.

——— Original Papers 2 Vols.

p. 53   Dalrymple's Annals of Scotland from the accession of Rob⁺ 1⁸⁺ to the Accession of the house of Stewart 2 Vols.

p. 181   The Case of Elisabeth claiming the Title & dignity of Countess of Sutherland.

Lying on the top

Sheet 3
p. 53   Dalrymple's Memoires concerning the provincial Councils of the Scots Clergy.

Memoires of G. B. & Ireland from the Dissolution of the last P. of Char. 2. until the Sea Battle of La Hogue by Sir In⁰ Dalrymple 2 Vols.

The New Natura Brevium, with Sir Mattheu Halis Commentary.

p. 13   Arnots History of Edinburgh.   *Removed to Locked Press*———

p. 29 (?) Blackston's Commentaries on the Laws of England 4 Vols.

p. 38   Burn's Ecclesiastical Law 2 Vols.

p. 97   Kaim's Sketches of the History of Man 2 Vols.

Universal Merchant.

†Considerations on the Trade & finances of this kingdom and on the measures of Administration.

p. 90   Humes Essays & Treatises on Several Subjects.   Vol 3

†Political Essays concerning the present State of the British Empire.

†Smith's Enquiry into the Nature and Causes of the Wealth of Nations 2 Vols.

†Another Coppy[*sic*] of the Same.

†Steuarts Enquiry into the principles of Political Oeconomy 2 Vols.

_____

† Crossed out.

Bonar

†Campbles Political Survey of G. Britain 2 Vols.
†Institutions Politiques la Baron de Bielfeld 2 Toms.
†Oeuvres de Montesquieu. 3 Toms.
Removed to Window Book Case _____

p. 1   Addisons Works 4 Vols.
p. 36   Jacobi Bruckeri Historia Critica Philosophiae 6 Toms.
        Marcus Meibomius Diogenis Laertii de Vitis Dogmatibus et
            Apophthegmatibus Clarorum Philosophorum G. &
            Latine 2 Toms.
p. 180 Strabonis Rerum Geographicarum G. & Latine. 2 Toms.

Sheet 4   **Left Hand Book Case**

                             Shelf 1ˢᵗ

p. 60   Drydens Works 4 Vols.
p. 40   Butlers Hudibras 2 Vols.
p. 39   ―――― Remains 2 Vols.
        Origin & Progress of Language. 3 Vols.
        Campbell's Philosophy of Rhetoric. 2 Vols.
        Hermes, or a Philosophical Enquiry concerning Language
            and Universal Grammar.
        Harrise's three Treatises, the first concerning Art, the second
            Music, Painting & Poetry, the third concerning happi-
            ness.
        ―――― Philosophical Arrangements.
p. 160 Oeuvres de Jean Jaques Rousseau Toms 10 & 11.
p. 32   M. Bouchaud de L'impôt ches les Romains.
        M. D'alembert Elemens de Musique.
p. 111 Malcolm's Treatise on Music.
p. 59   Tarif des Droits 2 Toms.
        Saxby's British Customs.
p. 107 Mackay's Abridgment of the Exise [*sic*] Laws &ᶜ.

                             Shelf 2..

† **Crossed out.**

Bonar	
	Historia del Concilio Tridentino di Pietro Soave Polano.
	L'ercolano Dialogo di M. Benedetto Varchi.
	Historia della Gverra Difiandra Bentivoglio.
p. 110 (?)	Malavolti Histoira di Siena.
p. 31	Il Decameron di Messer Giovanni Boccaccio.
Sheet 5	La Secchia Rapita Poemaeroicomico di Alessandro Tassoni 2 Toms.
p. 184	Di Pensieridiversi di Alessandro Tassoni.
p. 32	Orlando Innamorato de S Matteo Maria.
p. 42	De le Lettere Familiari de commendatore Annibal Caro.
	Opere del Marchese Beccaria Bonesana 3 Toms.
	Pieces Relatue A J. J. Rousseau.
p. 101	Lettres Populaires ou l'on examine la Reponse aux Lettres Ecrites de la Campagne.
	Responses Aux Lettres Populaires.
	Voltair's Dissertation sur la Gouvernement de Geneve.
	Solution Generale ou Lettres A. M. Covelle le fils Citoyen de Geneve.
	Erskin's Principles of Scots Law in the order of G. Mackenzies Institutes of that Law.
	Kaimses Abridgement of the Statute Law of Scotland.
p. 38	Burn's History of the Poor Laws.
p. 38	———— Justice of the Peace & Parish Officer 4 Vols.
	Etat Actuel des Finances.

Lying on the top

Generation Harmonique ou Traite de Musique.
Circulation et Credit Publique.
Lettre de la Campagne.

Shelf 3ᵈ

	Parlemens de Laroch.
p. 190	Vansittarts Narrative of the transactions in Bengal from the Year 1760 to 1764. 3 Vols.
Sheet 6	Scraftons observations on Vansittarts Narrative.
p. 118 (?)	De L'esprit des Loix 2 Toms.
	Considerations sur les causes de la Grandeur des Romains et de leur D'ecadence.

Bonar

Rousseau Citoyen de Geneve A Mʳ. D'alembert.
Les Amans Malheureux ou le Comte de Comminge.
L'affairs de Calas.
p. 1   Adam's principles of Latin & English Grammar.
p. 195   Ward's Essays upon the English Language.
Whites English Verb.
Lanctii Minerva.
Kaimses Elucidations of the Common and Statute Law of
Scotland.
(cf. p. 82) Heinecci Antiquitatum 2 Toms.
p. 81   Heineccius ad Pandectarum.
———— Ad Institutionum.
De Criminibus ad Commentarivs Antonii Matthaei.
p 48   Coccesi Jus Civile Controversum. 2 Vols.

Lying on the top

East India Examiner.

Shelf 4ᵗʰ

Castruccii Bonamici Commentariorum de Bello Italico   4 Vols
in two.
p. 32   *Castrucci Bonamici de Rebus ad Velitras Gestis Commentarius.
p. 160   Clarkes Rohaulti Physica Latine vertit recensuit & Adnota-
tionibus ex Illustrissimi Isaaci Newtoni.
Bonnets Considerations sur les Corps Organises.
———— Contemplations de la Nature.
Sheet 7
p. 191   Martyns Virgil 2 Vols.
p. 101   Linnaei Systema Naturae. 4 Vols.
p. 101   ———— Philosophia Botanica.
p. 101   ———— Genera Plantarum.
p. 101   ———— Species Plantarum. 2 Toms.
p. 155   Joannis Raii Synopsis Methodica Stirpium Britannicarum.
p. 100   Lees Introduction to Botany.
p. 180   Stillingfleets Miscellaneous Tracts relating to Natural History,
Husbandry, & Physic.

* Written on the verso of Sheet 5, and marked to be inserted here.

Bonar
p. 198
p. 140
p. 51

The British Zoology 4 Vols. Pennants Tower[sic].

Cronstedt's Essay towards a System of Mineralogy Translated from the original Swedish by Engestrom.

Wallerius's Mineralogy ou Description Generale des Substances du Regne Mineral 2 Toms.

On the top

Marine Dictionary.

Gordon's Geographical Grammar.

Shelf 5th

p. 160

Dempsteri Joannis Rosini Antiqvitartvm Romanarvm corpvs Absolvtissimvm cvm Notis.

Gronovii de Sestertiis.

Arnoldi Vinnii in Institutionum Imperialium Commentarius.

p. 68

Jo. Alberti Fabricii Bibliotheca Graeca 14 Vols. Vol. first qt. 2. Vol Secd 2. Vol. third 2. Vol. fourth 3. the remainder contains One Vol. each.

Sheet 8

Shelf 6th

Millers Gardeners Dictionary.

p. 142

Pitisco's Lexicon 3 Vols.

p. 180

Roberti Stephani Thesaurus Linguae Latine 4 Toms.

p. 165

Scott's Appendix ad Thesaurum Graecae Linguae ab Hen. Stephano Constructum 2 Vols.

p. 180

Stephani Thesaurus 4 Vols.

Scapulae's Lexicon Graeco Latinum Novum.

Right Hand Book Case

Shelf 1st

Philosophie Rurale ou Economie Generale et Politique de L'Agriculture.

Francheville's Histoira [sic] du Tarif de 1664. 2 Toms.

Bonar	
	Memoires Concernant les Impositions et Droips[sic] en Europe 4 Toms.
p. 8	Arbuthnot on Coins.
p. 47	Clark's Connection of the Roman, Saxon and English Coins.
	Essai sur les Memoires.
	Salzades Recueil des Monnoies.
	Bazinghen's Dictionnaire des Monnoies 2 Toms.
	Denisart Collections de Decisions 4 Toms.
	Ferrieres Dictionnaire de droit et de Pratique 2 To.
	Maillanes Dictionnaire de droit Canonique et de Pratique Beneficiale 2 Toms.
Sheet 9 p. 141	Pfeffels Nouvel Abrege Chronologique de la Histoire et du droit public D'allemagne 2 Toms.
	Schultingii's Jurisprudentia Ante-Justinianea.
p. 38	Petri Burmanni de Vectigalibus Populi Romani Dissertatio.
p. 107	Mackay's Excise Tables.
	Baldwin's Survey of the British Customs.
v. 194	Walpole's Historical Doubts on the Life & Reign of King Richard the Third.

Lying on the top

Proces-Verbal de ce qui s'Est Passe Au Lit De Justice, par Le Roi.

On the top

*Mackay's Excise Tables for Casting up the Duties on Strong, Small, & Two-penny Beer, as Now paid by the Common Brwers[sic] & Victuallers Respectively.

Shelf 2ᵈ

A Collection of Statutes Relating to Customs & Duties upon Salt Since the Year 1725.

Carkesses Book of Rates.

Statutes of Customs & Salt Duties from the Year 1734 to the Year 1775 inclusive 4 Vols.

Burrow's Book of Rates Vol 1.

---

* Written on the verso of Sheet 8, and marked to be inserted here.

Bonar

Statutes at Large from Magna Charta to the twentieth Year
of the Reign of King George the third inclu.^{ve} 13 V.
Cay's Abridgement of the Publick Statutes from Magna
Charta to the first Y.^{r} of G. the third inc. 2 Vols.
An Enquiry into the prices of wheat malt &.^{c} as sold in Eng-
land from the Year 1000 to 1765.
Instructions for Officers &.^{c} of his Majesty's Customs.

Lying on the top

p. 52

Instructions for Collectors &.^{c}
Rates of his Majesty's Customs.
Scots Acts Vol 3.

On the top

p. 52

*Sin's & Trewin's Rates of Merchandize as Settled by the
Acts of 12 Car: 2 Cap. 4. 2 Geo: 1 Cap. 7. And Sub-
sequent Acts of Parliament. With the Duties and
Drawbacks Payable on all Goods &.^{c},&.^{c}.———

Sheet 9
(verso)

Books in Uppermost Shelf
of Second Division

p. 56   Demosthenes Opera: Greek.
p. 13   Arriani Nicomediensis Expeditionsis Alexandri et Historia
Indica Jacobi Gronovii.
Lycophronis Ex ed: Ouon.
Pindari Olympia Nemea Pythia Isthmia.
.87   Horatii Lambi.
Doctrinae Particularum Linguae Graecae Auctore et Editore
Henrico Hoogeveen. 2 Toms.
.54   Novum Lexicon Graecum Etymologicum et Reale Chris-
tianus Tobias Damm 2 T.^{s}
p. 111   M. Manilii Astronomicon ex Recensione et cum Notis
Bentleii.
Papinii Silvarum Libri Qinque Jer: Marklandus.
p. 38   Burmanni Poetae Latini Minores 2 Toms.

* Written on the verso of Sheet 8, and marked to be inserted here.

Bonar

Valerius Flaccus Burmanni.

p. 38   Burmanni Anthologia 2 Toms. ——

p. 166   Casi Silii Italici Punicorum, Drakenborck.

Lucii Apuleii Madaurensis Platonici Philosophi Opera.

Auli Persii Flacci. Satirarum.

Horatius Flaccu Cum Commentariis. ——

Q. Ennii Poetiae Vetustissimi Fragmenta ——

Sheet 10

SECOND DIVISION

Upper Row

p. 2   *Æschyli Tragoediae Curante Joanne Cornelis de Pauw 2 Ts.

p. 67   Euripides Musgravii 4 Vols.

p. 144   Bryanus's Plutarchi Chaeronensis Vitae Parralelae cum singulis Aliquot Graece et Latine 5 Toms.

Remd Meibomius's Diogenis Laertii de Vitis, Dogmatibus et
Apophthegmatibus Clarorum Philosophorum. Greek and
Latin 2 Vols.

Lucian Samosatensis Opera, Greek & Latin 4 Toms.

p. 54   G. Daniel's Histoira de France 17 Toms.

La Grand's Histoira de la Milice Francoise. 2 Toms.

p. 155   Raynal's Histoira de la ville de Toulouse.

Lying on the top

p. 178   M. Spon's Histoira de Geneve 2 Toms.

Lying on the top

7   Dictionaire Francoise Latin et Italien Par M Antonini 2
Toms.

Left Hand Book Case

Shelf 1st

* Written on the verso of Sheet 9, and marked to be inserted here.

Bonar	
p. 67	Gilberts Treatise on the Court of Exchequer.
p. 29	Blackstones Analysis of the Laws of England.
	Finches Common Law ———
	A Treatise of affairs Maritime, & of Commerce.
p. 125	A Vol of Pamphlets.
p. 118	Considerations on Money, Bullion, & foreign Exchanges.
Sheet 11	Smith's Memoires of Wool 2 Vols.
p. 197	De Witts Political Maxims of the State of Holland.
p. 184	Temple's Works 4 Vols.
	Kippax Theory & Practice of Commerce and Maritime Affairs, translated from the Spanish of Don Geronymo de Uztariz 2 Vols.
	Three Tracts on the Corn-Trade & Corn-Laws.
p. 129	The Present Sate[sic] of G. Britain & N. America with regard to Agriculture, Population, Trade &c.
p. 59	Douglases Summary, Historical & Political, of the present State of the B. Settlements in N. A. 2 V.
p. 93	Hutchinson's History of the Colony of Massachusetts Bay 2 V.
	Smith's History of New York from the first discovery.
p. 140	An Historical Review of the Constitution & Government of Pennsylvania from its origin.
p. 150	Pownall on the Administration of the British Colonies 2 Vols.
	Burnaby's Travels through the Middle Settlements in North America in the Years 1759 & 60

Shelf 2ᵈ

	Marci Antonini Imperatoris.
p. 141	Pindari Carmina cvm Lectionis Varietate cvravit Christian Gottlob Heyne.
p. 85	Homeri Ilias & Odyssea Didymi 2 Toms.
p. 84	Clarkes Homeri Ilias 2 Toms. Homeri Opera Tom 2ᵈ.
	Hesiodi Ascraei quae exstant ex Recensione Graevii 2 Toms.
	Hutchinson's Xenophontis.
	——— ——— Xenophontis de Cyri Expeditione.
	Xenophontis Memorabilium Socrates Dictorum.

Bonar p. 65	Wolfio's Epicteti Stoici Philosophi Enchiridion. *Carried up* *Stairs.*
p. 66	—— —— Simplicii Commentarius in Enchiridion Epicteti.
Sheet 12 p. 56	Demetrii Phalerei de Elocutione, sive Dictione Rhetorica.
	Pearce's Dionysii Longini de Sublimitate Commentarius.
p. 94	Batties Isocratis Opera 2 Vols.
p. 106	Taylori's Lysiae Atheniensis Orationes. Greek & Latin.
	*Æschnis et Demosthenis Orationes de Carona.
p. 3	Needham's Geoponicorum Greek & Latin.
	Opuscula Mythologica Physica et Ethica Greek & Latin.
	Antiqvae Mvsicae Avctores Septem Gr. et Latine Marcvs Meibomivs.
	Wallises Claudii Ptolemaei Harmonicorum.
	Theocriti Moschi Bionis Simmii.

Lying on the top

Poesis Philosophica.

Novi Testamenti

Accesserunt Annotationes in Eratosthenem et Hymnos Dionysii.

Platonis Parmenidis

Kents Excerpta Quaedam ex Luciani Samosatensis Operibus.
Carried up Stairs.

Shelf 3ᵈ

p. 55	History of the National Debts.
p. 183	Symons Abridgement of the Excise Laws.
p. 90	Hume's History of England, & Essays 10 Vols.
	An Historical Dissertation concerning the Antiquity of the English Constitution.
Sheet 13 p. 98	Kerroux's Abrege de l'Histoire de la Hollande. 4 Toms.
p. 78	Hugonis Grotii de jure Belli ac Pacis 2 Toms.
	Pitisci's Q Curte Ressi Alexander Magnus et in illium Commentarius.
	Caii Suctonii Tranquilli ex recensione Francisci. Ouden-

---

* Written on the verso of Sheet 11, and marked to be inserted here.

Bonar	
	dorssii 2 Vols.
p. 165	L. Anaei Senecae Tragoediae.
p. 184	Terentii Comoediae.
p 184	Publii Terentii Api Comoediae Sex.
p. 144	Epistole Plinii.

On the top

p. 17	History of the Political Connection between England & Ireland from Y.ᵉ Reign of Henry 2ᵈ to the present time.
p. 120	A Collection of the Bills of Mortality from the Year 1659 to 1758 inclusive.

Shelf 4ᵗʰ

p. 122	Newtoni Principia Philosophiae.
p. 122	———— ———— Optice
p. 167	Roberti Simson opera Quaedam Geometrica Post Mortem eius impensis Philippi Comitis Stanhope
p. 72	Franklin's Experiments & observations on Electricity.
	M. Laurin's Treatise of Fluxions. 2 Vols.
	———— ———— Algebra.
p˙ 122	Newton's Method of Fluxions.
	———— ———— Arithmetica.
Sheet 14 p. 167	Simpson's Doctrine & Application of Fluxions 2 V.
p. 167	———— ———— Algebra.
p. 158	Robin's Mathematical Tracts 2 Vols.
p. 176	Smith's Philosophy of Musical Sounds.
p. 18	Barrow's Lectiones Opticae & Geometricae.
p. 167	Simson's Elements of Euclid.
	Discorsi et Dimostrazioni Mathematiche.
	Keill's Introduction to Natural Philosophy.
	———— ———— Introductio ad Astronomiam.
	Gregory's Arithmeticae et Algebra Compendium.
p. 77	———— ———— Practical Geometry.
p. 69	Ferguson's Tables & Tracts.
p. 150	Price on Annuities.
	Characteristics of the present Political State of G. Britain.
	Harris's Essay upon Money & Coins.

Bonar

Fleetwood's Chronicon Preciosum.

Lying on the top

p. 197

Wrights Elements of Trigonometry.
Mervilles Lexicon de Mathematiques.
Trail's Algebra.
Gregorio's Catoptricae et Dioptricae Sphaericae Elementa.

p. 37

*Histoire Naturelle, Generale et Particuliere Supplement par
M. Le Comte de Buffon   6 T$\underline{s}$.

Shelf 5$\underline{th}$

p. 37

Buffons Histoire Naturelle Generalle et Particuliere avec la
Description du Cabinet Du Roy   15 T$\underline{s}$.

p. 197

Winslow's Exposition Anatomique de la Structure du Corps
Humain.

Sheet 15
p. 111

Malcolms Arithmetic.

p. 164

Sandersons [*sic*] Elements of Algebra   2 Vols.

p. 167

Simsoni's Euclidis Elementorum.

p. 167

——— ——— ——— Sectionum Conicarum.

p. 167

——— ——— Apollonii Pergaei Locorum Planorum.

p. 21

Belidors la Science des Ingenieurs.
Ferguson's Lectures.

p. 105

De Luc's Recherches sur les Modifications de L'atmosphere
2 Toms.

On the top

p. 201

Hunters Medical Commentaries.
The Natural History of the Human Teeth by I. Hunter.

Shelf 6$\underline{th}$

Jacob's Law Dictionary.
Murray's Scots Laws & Acts of Parliament.
Erskine's Institute of the Law of Scotland on the order of
Sir Geo: Mackenzies Institutions of that Law ———.
M$\underline{c}$Douall's Institute of the Laws of Scotland in Civil Rights.

* Written on the verso of Sheet 13, and marked to be inserted here.

Bonar

3 Vols.

Stair's Institutions of the Law of Scotland deduced from its Originals.

p. 83   Defoe's History of the Union of G. Britain.

p. 16   Baillie's Cragii jus Feudale.

p. 48   Samuelis de Cocceii Introductio ad Henrici de Cocceii Grotium Illustratum.

p. 78   Henrici de Coccesi Grotius de jure Belli et[sic] Pacis   3 Toms.
Sheet 16
p. 165   Joannis Seldeni Mare Clausum seu de Dominio Maris.

Gothofredi Corpus Juris Civilis   2 Toms.

Right Hand Book Case

Shelf 1st

p. 96   Kalm's Travels into North America   3 Vols.

Remarks on the 13th. Parliament of G. Britain   Vol 1.

A Vol of Miscellanies.

. 146   Tuckers Reflections on the Naturalization of Foreign Protestants.

Three Vols of Political Phamphlets[sic].

. 198   Young's Political Arithmetic.

Cambridge's Account of the War in India from the Year 1750 to the Yr. 1761.

Holwell's Historical Events, Relating to the Provinces of Bengal & the Empire of Indostan.

The Investigator.

Patriot King.

A Dissertation Upon Parties.

p. 106   Lytteltons Dialogues of the Dead.

p. 45   Chesterfields Letters to his Son   4 Vols.

Sheet 17   Leland's History of the Life & Reign of Philip King of Macedon   2 Vols.

Hampton's General History of Polybuis, Translated from the Greek   4 Vols.

Shelf 2d

Bonar

p. 8

p. 105

p. 8

Oratorum Graecorum   12 Vols.

Hoelzlino Apollonii Rhodii Argonauticorum.

Luciani Samosatensis Opera. 2 Vols.

Tollius's Appiani Alexandrini Romanarum Historiarum
2 Toms.

Callimachi Hymni et Epigrammata.

Shelf 3ᵈ

Theocriti Idylliorum.

Alexandri ab Alexandro Genialium Dierum 2 Toms.

p. 143
M. Acci Plauti Comoediae Accedit Commentarivs.

Pvb. Ovidii Nasonis 3 Toms.

M & L. Annaei Senecae Opera 3 Toms.

p. 143
C. Plinii Secundi Naturalis Historiae 3 Toms.

p. 183
C. Cornelii Taciti Opera 2 Toms.

Sheet 18

Shelf 4ᵗʰ

Aristotelis de Rhetorica.

p. 177
Sophoclis Tragoediae 2 Vols in one.

p. 2
Aeschyli Tragoediae 2 Toms.

Omnia Pindari 2 Toms.

Marci Antonini Imperatoris 2 Vols.

Xenophontis de Agesilao Rege Oratio.

p. 185
Theophrasti Characteres. Ethici.

p. 67
Euripidis Orestes.

Theognidis Phocylidis Phythagorae.

Winterton's Poetae Minores.

Isocrates Graece.

p. 144
Plutarchi Chaeronensis Parallela seu Vitae Parallelae.

p. 144
——— ——— 3 Toms.

p. 144
——— ——— Chaeronensis quae extant Opera cum
Latina Interpretatione 3 Vols.

p. 82
Herodiani Historiarum.

p. 96
Cantel's Justinus de Historiis Philippicis et Totius Mundi
Originibus.

p. 163
Crispinus Salustii Opera.

T. Livii Platavini Historiarum ab Vrbe Condita 3 Toms.

Shelf 5th

An Essay for the Amendment of the Silver Coins.
Leake's Historical Account of English Money from the Conquest to the present time.
Bindon's Political Essay upon Commerce, Translated from the french [*sic*].

p. 197 Wrights American Negotiator.
Moivres Annuities on Lives.
p. 167 Simpson's Elemens de Geometrie.
p. 186 Tiphaigne Essai sur L'Histoire Œconomique des Mers Occid
Entails de France.
p. 80 Guischardt's Memoires Militaires sur les Grecs et les Romains 2 Toms.
p. 118 Memoire di Montecuccoli.
p. 69 Memoires de M. Le, Marqquis de Feuquiere 4 Toms.
p. 76 Memoires de M. de Gourville 2 Toms.
p. 46 Choisy's Memoires pour servier A L'Histoire de Louis 14.
p. 105 Memoires et Reflexions sur les Principaux Evenemens du Regne de Louis 14.
p. 178 Memoires de Madame de Staal 4 Toms.
p. 195 Histoire du Ministere du Chevalier R. Walpool 3 T.
Essai Politique sur la Pologne.
p. 139 Pattullo's Essai sur L'amelioration des Terres.
Plaidoyer's et Oeuvres Diverses de M. Patru 2 Toms.

Shelf 6th

Dalrymple's Essay towards a General History of Feudal Property in G. Britain.
Innes's Critical Essay on the Ancient Inhabitants of Scotland 2 Vols.
Memoires Concerning the Affairs of Scotland from Queen Annes Accession to the Throne, to the commencement of the Union of the two Kingdoms of Scotland & England in the Yr. 1707.

Bonar p. 112	Martin's Description of the Western Islands of Scot<u>d</u>. Lindsay's History of Scotland from the Year 1436 to 1565, to which is added a Continuation by another hand till Aug<u>t</u>. 1604. Dalrymple's Remarks on the Hist. of Scotland.
p. 39	Burnets History of his own Time 6 Vols.
p. 111	Markland's Remarks on the Epistles of Cicero. Famiani Stradae Prolusiones Academicae. Rollin's Quintiliani Institutionum Oratoriarum 2 T.
p. 87	Horatii Flacci Poemata. Quintus Horatius Flaccus. ——— ——— Horatii Flacci Carmina Expurgata 2 T. Marshall's Juvenal.
p 191	P. Virgilii Maronis Opera 3 Toms.
p. 186	Tibullus et Propertius.
p. 105	Titus Lucretius Carus.
p. 141	Phaedri Augusti Liberti Fabularum.

Sheet 21   Shelf 7<u>th</u>

p. 75	Girard [*sic*] Trois Livres des Offices de France 2 Toms.
p. 139	Les Recherches de la France D'estienne Pasqvier.
p. 18	Beaumanoirs Coustumes de Beauvoisis.
p. 60	Drummond of Hawthorndens Works, from the Original Copies. Cassendi Opera 6 Toms. Joannis Stobaei Eclogarum.
p. 180	Stobaeum Loci Communes.

Sheet 21
(verso)   Uppermost Row of Third Division

p. 8	Apollonii Rhodius 2 Toms. Oppian Schneider. ——— Callimachi Hymni Epigrammata et Fragmenta, Jo: Augustus Ernesti. 2 Toms. Analecta Veterum Poetarum Graecorum Phil. Brunch 3 Toms.

Sheet 22   **THIRD DIVISION**

Bonar

Upper Row

p. 7	Dictionaire Italien, Latin, et Francois par M. Antonini.
p. 144	Plutarco Opuscoli Morali Trad et Gandini 2 T *2 Toms* *Ly'g on ye Top*
p. 54	Historia delle Guerre Civili di Francia di Davila 2 Toms. Istorici delle Cose Veneziane 10 Toms.
p. 73	Istoria della Repubblica di Venezia in tempo Della Sacralega di Garzoni 2 Vols. Principi di Storia Civile della Repubblica di Venezia 6 Vols. Istoria Civile del Regno di Napoli di Geannone 5 Vols.
p. 23	Relationi del Bentivoglio.
. 5	Istrorie [*sic*] Fiorentine di Scipione Ammirato 3 Vols.
p. 190	Storia Fiorentina di Messer Benedetto Varchi. Della Storia di Genova.
p. 183	La Gierusalemme Liberata di Torquato Tasso 2 Toms.
p. 152	H Morgante Maggiore del Pulci. Ricciardetto di Niccolo Carteromaco 2 Vols in one.

Sheet 23

Left Hand Book Case

Shelf 1st

p. 149	Warburton's Edition of Popes Works 9 Vols with a Supplement.
p. 186	Tindal's Continuation of Rapin's History of England from the Revolution to the present times 9 Vols.
	The Annual Register, or a view of the History, Politicks, Literature, from the Year 1758, to the Year 1778 inclusive 21 Vols.
	*The Annual Register, for the Year 1779 Vol 22. Vols 23, 24.

Front Row

An Essay on the Writings and Genius of Pope.

---

* Written on the verso of Sheet 22, and marked to be inserted here.

Bonar p. 183	Orrery's Remarks on the Life & Writings of Swift.
p. 3	Akenside's Poems.
p. 95	Johnson's Lives of the most Eminent English Poets; with Critical observations on their Works 4 Vols.

Shelf 2$\underline{d}$

p. 95	The Rambler 4 Vols.
	——— ——— Idler 2 Vols.
	The Man of the World 2 Vols.
	——— ——— Man of Feeling.
Sheet 24	——— ——— Julia de Roubigne, A Tale 2 Vols.
p. 182	Swifts Works, With a Supplement 10 Vols.
p. 179	The Tatler 4 Vols.
p. 1	——— Spectator 8 Vols.
p. 81	Hamilton's Poems.

Lying on the top

	Ramsay's Poems. 2 Vols.
	——— ——— Ever-Green, being A Collection of Scots Poems 2 V$\underline{s}$.
p. 17	Bannatynes Ancient Scottish Poems.

Front Row

	The Poems of Philips, Smith & Pomfret.
p. 165	Ancient and Modern Scottish Songs 2 Vols.
p. 118	The Mirror A Periodical Paper published at Edin$\underline{r}$. in the Years 1779 and 1780 3 V$\underline{s}$.
p. 76	Goldsmith's Poetical & Dramatick Works 2 Vols.

Shelf 3$\underline{d}$

p. 179	The Guardian 2 Vols.
p. 89	Humes Essays 4 Vols.
p. 116	Miltons Paradise Lost.
p. 116	——— ——— Regain'd.
p. 185	Thomson's Works 4 Vols.
Sheet 25	Priors Poems 2 Vols.

Wilkies Epigoniad, A Poem in Nine Books.

———— ———— Fables.

Jonses Poems, Consisting chiefly of Translations from the Asiatick Languages.

Reliques of Ancient English Poetry 3 Vols.

Avison's Essay on Musical Expression.

Rouquets present State of the Arts in England.

Thomas's British Negotiator.

An Essay on the Causes of the Decline of the Foreign Trade.

Gee on the Trade & Navigation of Great-Britain.

Child on Trade.

Mun's Englands Treasure by Foreign Trade.

Tucker's Essay on Trade.

Law on Trade.

———— ———— Proposals & Reasons for Constituting a Council of Trade in Scotland.

A General Description of all Trades.

The Dublin [sic] Society's Weekly Observations, for the Advancement of Agriculture and Manufactures.

Lying on the top

History of Peg, only lawful Sister to John Bull Esqr..

Mortimer's Every Man his own Broker.

Scottish Tragic Ballads.

Logan's Poems.

Shelf 4th

Potter's Greician Antiquities 2 Vols.

Kennets Roman Antiquities.

Les Poesies de Catvlle [sic] de Verone.

Quintus Horatius Flaccus.

Emendationes et Supplementa Liviana.

Lettres de Ciceron A. Atticus Par M. Mongault 6 T.

M. Tullii Ciceronis Opera Omnia di Verburgius 11 T.

On the top

Chapman's Essay on the Roman Senate.

Bonar

Middleton's Treatise on the Roman Senate.
Ciceronis Academica.

Front Row

p. 87   Q Horatii Flacci Poemata.   Alexander Cuningamius
2 Toms.

Shelf 5th

p. 171   Theorie des Sentimens Moraux, Translated from the English
par M. Blavet 2 Tom.

p. 171   Smiths Moralischen Empfindungen.   Another Coppie of the
Same.

p. 170   Metaphysique de L'Ame: ou Theorie des Sentimens Moraux
2 Toms.

Sheet 27
p. 95   Pieces Sur Le Jesuite 4 Toms.

Compte Rendu des Constitutions des Jesuites par M de la
Chalotais.

Memoire Sur l'Institut et la Doctrine des Jesuites.

p. 134   Remonstrances du Parlement Au Roi.

p. 137   Remonstrances du Parlement de Normandie.

p. 137   ——— ——— ——— de la Cour Des Comptes, Aydes
et Finances de Normandie.

p. 136   Arretes et Objets de Remonstrances de la cour des Compts
aydes et Finances de Montpellier.

Recit de L'Affaire du Parlement de Dauphine.

Recueil des Arretes Remonstrances et Autres Pieces.

Comptes des Constitutions et de la Doctrine de la Societe se
disant de Jesus par M Charles.

p. 132   Remontrances du Parlement de Toulouse Au Roi.

p. 133   Secondes Remonstrances du Parlement de Provence.

p. 136   Arrestes et Remontrances de la Chambre des Comptes.

p. 131   Remontrances du Parlement de Rouen.

p. 131   ——— ——— ——— de la cour des Aides de Montau-
ban.

p. 135   Actes de l'Assemblee Generale du Clerge de France sur la
Religion.

p. 130   Arrests, Arrestes et Remontrances du Parlement de Bordeaux.

Le Veritable Usage de l'autorite Seculiere dans les Matieres

Bonar	qui Concernent la Religion par M.D.P.
	Observations sur Le Memoire de M. Guettard Concernant la Porcelaine.
	Reflexion d'un Avocat sur les Remontrances du Parlement.
Sheet 28	*Lying on the top*
p. 132	Remontrances de Toulou.
p. 134	————— ————— ————— du Parlement Au Roi.
	Proces pour la Succession d'Ambroise Guys Contre les Jesuites.
	Shelf 6ᵗʰ
p˙ 106	Des Principes des Negociations par M. de Mably.
p. 106	Le Droit Public de l'Europe Fonde sur les Traitis [*sic*] par M. de Mably 3 T.
p. 106	Observations sur l'Histoire de France par M. de Mably 2 Toms.
	Observations sur les Romains par M de Mably. 2 T.
	————— ————— ————— Sur Les Grecs par M. de Mably.
p. 106	————— ————— ————— Sur l'Histoire de la Grece ou des Causes de la Prosperite et des Malheurs des Grecs par M. de Mably.
Sheet 29 p. 106	Entretiens de Phocion, sur la Rapport de la Morale Avec La Politique par M. de Mably.
	Recherche de la Verite 3 Toms.
	Traite du Beaw [*sic*] par J. P. de Crousaz 2 Toms.
p. 49	Origine des Connoissance Humaines par Condillac.
	Traite des Sensations par M. de Condillac 2 Toms.
p. 49	Traites des Sistemes par Condillac 2 Toms.
	Traite des Animaux par M. de Condillac.
p. 151	Essai de Psychologie.
p. 32	Traite d'Insectologie par M. Bonnet.
p. 108	Elemens de Chymie—Theorique par M. Macquer.
p. 184	La Philosophie Applicable A Tous les objects de l'Esprit et de la Raison par M. Terrasson.
p. 185	Les Characteres de Theophraste 2 Toms.
p. 65	Principes Generaux la Education de la Noblesse Francoise

3 Toms.
Maxims et Reflexions Morales de Rochefoucauld.

Shelf 7th

p. 84 Homeri Ilias 2 Vols.
p. 85 ——— ——— Odyssea 2 Vols.
p. 142 Platonis Opera, Greek & Latin 3 Vols.
Sheet 30 Xenophontis Opera.
p. '10 Aristotelis Opera Omnia Qva Extant Gr. Lat. 4 Vols.
p. 165 Sexti Empirici Opera di Fabricius. Gr. Lat.
p. 10 Aristophanis Comediae Undecim Graece et Latine.
Philostratorum qvae Supersunt Omnia. Gottefridus Olearius.
Gr. Lat.

Right Hand Book Case

Shelf 1st

Gazette Litteraire de l'Europe 7 Toms.

Front Row

Bibliotheque Choise povr servir de Svite A La Bibliotheque
Universelle par Jean Le Clerc. 25 T.

p 66 L'Espion Anglois, ou Correspondance Secrete Entre Milord
All'eye et Milord All'ear 4 Toms.

p. 113 Journal Historique de la Revolution Operee dans la Constitution de la Monarchie Francoise, par M. de Maupeow
7 Toms.

Lying on the top

Memoires concernant L'Administration des Finances, sous Le
Ministere de M L'Abbe Terrai.

Sheet 31 Shelf 2d

p. 165 Recueil des Lettres de Madame La Marquise de Sevigne

Bonar

    9 Toms.

    Lettres de Madame de Maintenon 9 Toms. Each of the
        first four Toms contains two, the last One Tom.

    Memoires pour Servir a l'Histoire de Madame de Maintenon
        6 Toms. Two Toms in Each of the three.

p. 39   Memoires de Messire Roger de Rabutin Comte de Bussy
        9 Toms.

p. 6   Memoires pour servir A l'Histoire D'Anne. ———— D'Au-
        triche par Madame de Motteville 6 Toms.

Lying on the top

    Oeuvres de Madame La Marquise de Lambert.

p. 33   Soins Faciles pour La Proprete de la Bouche et pour la Con-
        servation des Dents par M. Bourdet.

p. 59   Douglas's Comparitive [*sic*] Description of all the Muscles
        in a Man, & in a Quadruped.

    Cullen's Institutions of Medicine

Front Row

p. 66   Lettres, Memoirs et Negociations de M. Le Comte d'Estrades
        9 Toms.

p. 15   Negociations de Monsieur le Comte D'Avaux 6 Toms.

p. 7   *L'Intrigue du Cabinet, sous Henry 4th et Louis 13th
        Terminee par La Frond par M. Anquetil 4 Toms————

p. 158   Memoires de la Minorite de Louis 14. par M. Rochfaucauld
        2 Toms.

    Histoire du Roy Henry Le Grand par Perefixe.

Sheet 32   Shelf 3d

    Lettres sur les Anciens Parlemens [*sic*] de France par M. de
        Boulainvilliers 3 Toms.

p. 33   Essais sur la Noblesse de France, par M. Boulainvilliers.

    Etat de la France, par Comte de Boulainvilliers 8 Toms.

    Lettres Historiques sur Le Parlement sur le droit des Pairi
        3 Toms.

    Institution Au Droit Francois par M. Argon. 2 Toms.

---

* Written on the verso of Sheet 30, and marked to be inserted here.

Bonar

Histoire du Droit Public Ecclesiastique Francois par M.D.B.
2 T.

p. 10   Institution Au Droit Ecclesiastique par M. Fleury. 2 Toms.

p. 124   Les Origines, ou l'Ancien Gouvernement, de la France, de
L'Allemagne et de l'Italie 4 Toms.

p. 60   Histoire Critique de l'Etablissement de la Monarchie Francoise Dans Les Gaules. par M. Dubos 4 Toms.

Histoire de la Ligue Faite A Cambray 2 Tom.

Sheet 33   *Lying on the top*

Remarques sur Plusieurs Branches de Commerce et de Navigation.

Considerations sur le Gouvernement, Ancien et Present de
la France par Marquis Argenson.

p. 88   An Account of the Ancient Free State of France Translated
from the Latin of Hotoman.

Le Code Noir ou Recueil des Reglemens Rendus.

p. 61   Code de la Police ou Analyse des Reglemens de Police par
M. Duchesne.

Front Row

†Constitutio Nes Societa Tis Jesu.
Practica Criminalis P. Sanctorvm de Melfi.
Constitutio Nes Societa Tis Jesu.
Regulae Societatis Jesu.

Sheet 34   Shelf 4th

Meditazioni Sulla Economia Politica.
Elements D'Agriculture par M. Monceau 2 Toms.
Prairies Artificielles.
Recherches Sur la Valeur des Monnoies.

p. 82   Essai sur la Police des Grains par Herbert.
Essai Politique sur Le Commerce.
Reflexions Politiques sur les Finances, et Le Commerce.
2 Toms.
Examen du Relflexions[sic] Politiques sur les Finances et le

† Struck out by a straight stroke.

Bonar

Commerce 2 Toms.

Essai sur la Nature du Commerce en General.

L'Ami des Hommes, ou Traite de la Population 5 Toms.

Essais Sur les Ponts et Chaussees La Voirie et les Corvees 2 Toms.

p. 7   L'Anti-Financier.

Le Reformateur ou Nouveau Profet.

Elemens du Commerce 2 Toms.

Recherches et Considerations sur les Finances de France 6 Toms.

Principes et Observations Oeconomiques 2 T.

Le Commerce et Le Gouvernement par M. de Condillac.

L'Ordre Naturel et Essentiel des Societes Politiques 2 Toms.

Sheet 35   *Lying on the top*

p. 120   Prospectus D'un Nouveau Dictionnaire de Commerce par Morellet.

p. 120   Refutation de L'ouvrage qui a pour titre Dialogues sur le Commerce Des Bleds.

Sur La Legislation et le Commerce des Grains.

Thorie [*sic*] de l'Impot.

Shelf 5th

p. 2   Journal de L'Agriculture du Commerce et des Finances 9 Toms.

p. 152   Physiocratie ou Constitution Naturelle du Gouvernement le plus Avantageux au genre Humain, par Quesnay 2 Toms.

Sheet 36   Recueil de Plusieurs Morceaux Economiques par M Trosne.

Ephemerides du Citoyen ou Bibliotheque Raisonnee des Sciences Morales et Politiques 6 Toms. Each of the Three Toms contains Two.

Ephemerides du Citoyen ou Bibliotheque Raisonnee des Sciences Morales et Politiques 1767. 12 Toms in four.

The Same Book Continued for 1768. 12 Toms in four.

The Same for 1769. 12 Toms in four.

Bonar

Lying on the top

Journal de L'Agriculture du Commerce et des Finances for
Oct: 1766.
Meditazioni sulla Economia Politica.
Considerations Sur les Finances d'Espagne.

Sheet 37   Shelf 6th

p. 181   Memoires de Sully Principal Ministre de Henry Le Grand
          8 Toms.
          Nouvel Abrege Chronologique de L'Histoire de France.
p. 190   Histoire Generale de L'Europe sous Le Regne de Louis 13
          par M: Vassor. 10 Toms.

Lying on the top

Lettres Ecrites de la Montagne par Rousseau.

Sheet 38   Shelf 7th

p. 57   Diodori Siculi Bibliothecae Historicae Libri qui Supersunt
          Petrus Wesselingius 2 Vols.
p. 57   Casii Dionis Historiæ Romanae 2 Vols.
          Dionysii Halicarnassei Scripta Qvae Exstant Omnia et His-
          torica et Rhetorica.
          Dionysii Halicarnassei Tomvs 2 Rhetoricos eivs et Criticos
          Libros Continens.
          Julii Pollucis Onomasticum Gr. & Latin 2 Vols.
          Dictionnaire des Arrets, ou Jurisprudence Universelle des
          Parlemens [sic] de France 6 Toms.

Sheet 39   **FOURTH DIVISION**

                                Upper Row

p. 46   M. Tullii Ciceronis Opera cum Delectu Commentariorum
          9 Toms.

Bonar	
p. 105	Titi Lucretii Cari de Rerum Natura Libri Sex.
p. 191	Publii Virgillii Maronis Bucolica Georgica et Æneis.
p. 186	Catulli Tibulli et Propertii Opera.
p. 164	Julii Cae Saris [*sic*] Scaligeri viri Clarissimi.
p. 158	Robertson's History of Scotland during the Reigns of Queen Mary & of King James 6th till his Accession to the Croun [*sic*] of England 2 Vols.
p. 158	——— ——— History of the Reign of the Emperor Charles 5th, with a view of the progress of Society in Europe, from the Subversion of the Roman Empire, to the beginning of the Sixteenth Century 3 Vols.
p. 195	Watson's History of the Reign of Philip the Second, King of Spain 2 Vols.
p. 140	Pennants Tour in Scotland 3 Vols.
	Etats Formes en Europe Apres La Chute de l'Empire Romain en occident par d'Anville.
Sheet 40	Notice de l'Ancienne Gaule, par d'Anville.
p. 8	Analyse Geographique de l'Italie, par d'Anville.
	Memoires sur l'Egypte Ancienne et Moderne. par d'Anville.

Lying above

p. 8	Antiquite Geographique de L'Inde p d'Anville.
p. 22	Bell's Travels from St. Petersburg in Russia to diverse parts of Asia 2 Vols.
p. 190	Verelst's View of the Rise, Progress, & Present State of the English Government in Bengal.
p. 32	Bolt's Considerations on the present State of Bengal & its Dependances [*sic*].
p. 49	Cook's Voyaage[*sic*] towards the South Pole & Round the World, in the Years 1772, 73, 74, & 75. 2 Vols.
p. 44	Voyages du Chevalier Chardin en Perse et Autres Lieux de l'Orient 4 Toms.
	Histoire Philosophique et Politique des Indes 3 Toms.
p. 124	Orme's History of the Military transactions of the British Nation in Indostan from the Year 1745. 2 Vols.
p. 74	Halbed's[*sic*] Translation of the Gentoo Code of Laws ———
p. 110	Joannis Petri Maffeii Historiarum Indicarum.

Bonar

Sheet 41
p. 50

p. 84

p. 43

Lying on the top

Cordiners Antiquities & Scenery of the North of Scotland in a series of Letters to Thomas Pennant.

Holwell's India Tracts.
follows Watson's Hist!

Chalmers's Political Annals of the Present United Colonies, from their Settlement to the Peace of 1763.

Left Hand Book Case

Shelf 1st

p. 54
p. 81
p. 188
p. 198
p. 197

Sheet 42
p. 198

p. 198

p. 28

p. 58

D'Avenant's Political & Commercial Works   5 Vols.

Harte's Essays on Husbandry.

Tull's Essay on the Principles of Vegetation and Tillage.

Young's Farmers Letters   2 Vols.

————   ————   ———— Six Weeks Tour through the Southern Counties of England & Wales.

————   ———— Six Months Tour through the North of England   4 Vols.

————   ———— Tour through the East of England   4 Vols.

Birches Life of Henry Prince of Wales Eldest Son of King James I.

Dossie's Memoirs of Agriculture & other Oeconomical Arts   2 Vols.

Macbride's Experimental Essays on Medical and Philosophical Subjects.

Priestley's Experiments and observations on Different kinds of Air   2 Vols.

Ferguson's Introduction to Electricity.

Sheet 43

Shelf 2d

Traite des Mesures Itineraires Anciennes et Modernes par M. D'Anville.

Memoire sur la Chine par d'Anville.

Bonar	
p. 8	L'Empire Turc Considere dans son Etablissement et dans ses Accroissemens Successifs par D'Anville.
p. 8	Geographie Ancienne Abregee par M d'Anville 3 Toms.
	Le Siecle de Louis 14, par M. Francheville 2 Toms.
	Melanges d'Histoire et de Litterature par M. de Vigneul-Marville 3 T.
p. 88	Histoire du Gouvernement de Venise par Houssaie 3 Toms.
	La Voix Libre du Citoyen, ou Observations sur la Gouvernement de Pologne 2 T.
p. 95	Etat Present de la Republique des Provinces-Unies et des Pais qui en Dependent. par Janicon 2 Toms.
p. 74	Edits de la Republique de Geneve.
p. 167	Josiae Simleri de Republica Helvetiorum Auctore J Conrado Fueslino.
	Histoire de la Confederation Helvetique par M de Watteville.
p. 161	Histoire de la Reformation de la Suisse par Ruchat 6 Toms.
	Tableau Historique et Politique de la Suisse.
p. 186	L'Etat et Les Delices de la Suisse 4 Toms.

Lying on the top

Sheet 44 p. 7	Proposition D'une Mesure de la Terre par M. D'Anville.
p. 98	Keate's Account of the Ancient History, present Government, & Laws of the Republic of Geneva.
	An Account of Switzerland. Written in y̲ᵉ Y̲ʳ 1714.
	An Enquiry into the connection between the present price of provisions and the size of Farms.

Shelf 3

p. 166	Shakespeare's Plays With all the Various Readings, & Notes by Johnson & Steevens 12 Vols.
	Œuvres de M̲ʳ De Maupertius. 4 Toms.
Sheet 45 p. 158	De La Nature par J. Robinet 3 Toms. *follows La Mendicite front Row.*
	De La Felicite Publique 2 Toms.
	Systeme de la Nature par M. Mirabaud 2 T.
	La Politique Naturelle, par un Ancien Magistrat 2 Toms.
p. 183	Systeme Social. ou Principes Naturels de la Morale et de la

Bonar

Politique.

De L'Homme de ses Facultes Intellectuelles et de Son Education par Helvetius. 2 Toms.

p. 66   Essays and Observations, Physical & Literary.   Read before
a Society in Edinburgh, & Published by them   2 Vols.

p. 172   A: Smith's National-Reichthuemer.   *follows La Nature
front Row.* ———

L'Analyze des Echecs par Philidor.

Lying on the top

Richardson's Philosophical Analysis & Illustration of some
of Shakespear's Remarkable Characters.

Hamilton's Observations on Mount Vesuvius, Mount Etna,
& other Volcanos.

p. 138   Pensees de M. Pascal.

Front Row

p. 73   Davies's Memoires of the Life of D. Garrick   2 Vols.

An Apology for the Life Colley Cibber, Comedian, With an
Historical View of the Stage during his own time,
Written by Himself   2 Vols.

p. 174   *M: Blavet's french Translation of Smith's Enquiry into the
Nature and Causes of the Wealth of Nations   3 Vols.

Les Moyens de Detruire La Mendicite En France.

Sheet 46   Shelf 4ᵗʰ

Cudworths Treatise Concerning Eternal & Immutable
Morality.

p. 102   Locke's Essay Concerning Human Understanding   2 Vols.

Watts Logick.

p. 102   Locke's Two Treatises of Government.

p. 69   Fletcher's Political Works.

The Religion of Nature Delineated.

p. 166   Shaftesbury's Characteristicks of Men, Manners, Opinions,
Times.   3 Vols.

An Enquiry into the Original of our Ideas of Beauty &

—————

* Written on the verso of Sheet 44, and marked to be inserted here.

Bonar	Virtue.
p. 92	Hutcheson's Esasy on the Nature & Conduct of the passions & Affections.
p. 89	A Treatise of human Nature: Being an attempt to Introduce the Experimental Method of Reasoning into Moral Subjects. 3 Vols.
Sheet 47 p. 168	Smith's Theory of Moral Sentiments: to which is added a Dissertation on the Origin of Languages.
	Prices Review of the Principal Questions and Difficulties in Morals.
	Kaimes British Antiquities.
	——— ——— Historical Law-Tracts 2 Vols.
	——— ——— Elements of Criticism 3 Vols.
p. 155	Reids Enquiry into the Human Mind, on the principles of Common Sense.
	Beatties Essays on the Nature & immutabiility[*sic*] of Truth, in opposition to Sophistry & Septicism [*sic*] 2 Vols.
p. 99	Principles of Penal-Law ———.
	Dunbar's Essays on the History of Mankind in Rude and Cultivated Ages.

Lying on the top

	Kaim's Essays on the Principles of Morality and Natural Religion.
p. 176	Smith's Select Discourses.
	King's Inquiry into the Nature and Origin of Evil.
	A Memorial Addressed to the Sovereigns of Europe on the present State of Affairs between the old & New World.
p. 5	The Rights of G. Britain Asserted against the Claims of America.

Front Row

p. 164	Poetarum Scotorum Musae Sacrae. 2 Vols. *Removed.*
Sheet 48	Jo. Barclaii Argenis 2 Vols in One. *Removed.*
p. 17	——— ——— ——— Satyricon. *Removed.*
	Lalius And Hortensiae; Or Thoughts on the Nature & objects of Taste & Genius, in a Series of Letters To Two friends.
p. 187	Tucker's Treatise Concerning Civil Government.

Bonar p. 65	Kaim's Loose Hints Upon Education, Chiefly Concerning the Culture of the Heart.
	An Essay Upon Tune, being an attempt to free the Scale of Music & the Tune of Instruments, from Imperfection.

Shelf 5th

p. 154	M Fabii Quinctiliani de Institutione Oratoria & Ejusdem Declamationes per Petro Burmanno 2 Vols.
p. 140	Titi Petronii Satyricon Qvae Supersunt Petro Burmanno 2 Vols.
	*Observations upon the Riot Act with an attempt towards its amendment.
Sheet 49 p. 75	*Zero's Succinct Review of the American Contest ―――
	Scriptores Rei Rusticae, Jo Matthia Gesnero 2 Toms.
	Le Rime del Petrarca, per Ludovico Castelvetro 2 Vols.
p. 118	Les Essais de Michel Seigneur De Montaigne par Pierre Coste. 3 Toms.
p. 154	Œuvres de Racine 2 Toms.
p. 56	Œuvres Dramatiques de Nericault Destouches 4 Toms.
p. 77	Grays Poems.

Shelf 6th

Vocabolario Degli Accademici Della Crusca 6 Toms.

Dictionnaire de L'Academie Francoise 2 Toms.

Johnson's Dictionary of the English Language 2 Vols.

Postlethwayt's Universal Dictionary of Trade and Commerce. 2 Vols.

cf. p. 6)	Anderson's, Historical & Chronological Deduction of the Origin of Commerce, from the Earliest Accounts to the present Time. 2 Vols.

Sheet 50   **Right Hand Book Case**

Shelf 1st

* Written on the verso of Sheet 47, and marked to be inserted here.

Bonar	
p. 2	Æschyli Tragoediae sex.
p. 67	Euripides Tragoediae 2 Toms.
	†Epicteti Enchiridion.
p. 177	Sophoclis Tragoediae
p. 65	Epicteti Enchiridion.
p. 83	Historiae Augustae Scriptorum Minorum Latinarum[sic] 4 Vols.
p. 49	Republica di Venetia del Cardinal Contarini.
	Elementa Philosophica de Cive Auctore Thom: Hobbes.
p. 157	Testament Politique du Cardinal duc de Richelieu.
	Hugo Grotius de Veritate Religionis Christianae Joannis Clerici.
p. 1	Memoires de L'Academie des Sciences.
p. 185	Œuvres Diverses de Mr. Thomas.
p. 70	Les Interets de la France Mal Entendus par un Citoyen 2 Toms.
	L'Antropologie Traite Metaphysique par M. le Marquis de Gorini Corio 2 Toms.
	Synopsis Metaphysicae Ontologiam et Pneumatologiam Complectens.
Sheet 51	Ethica Huchesoni.
p. 91	――― ――― Introduction to Moral Philosophy.
	Des Corps Politiques et de Leurs Gouvernements 2 Toms.
	The Works of Francis Rebelais 5 Toms.

Lying on the top

Anacreontis Carmina cum Sapphonis et Alcaei Fragmentis.
Another Coppie of the same.

Shelf 2d

p. 87	Q Horatii Flacci Epistola ad Augustum.
	Poetique Francoise par M. Marmontel 2 Toms.
	Les Quatre Poetiques par M. Batteux 2 Toms.
p. 60	Reflexions Critiques Sur la Poesie et Sur la Peinture par M Du Bos. 3 T.
p. 18	Principes de la Litterature par M. Batteux 5 Toms.

† Struck out by a straight stroke.

Bonar *Sheet 52* p. 56	Œuvres Philosophiques et Dramatiques De M. Diderot 6 Toms. Cours de Peinture par Principes, par M.ʳ de Piles. Abrege de la Vie des Peintres par M. De Piles.
p. 187	Histoire Litteraire des Troubadours 3 Toms.
p. 31	Ragguagli di Parnaso del Signor Trajano—Boccalini Romano 2 Toms. Historiae de l'Universite de Paris 7 Toms.

Lying on the top

p. 17	Baretti's Italien Library.
p. 156	Reflexions Historiques et Critiques sur les Differens Theatres de L'Europe, par Riccoboni.
p. 36	Bruces First Principles of Philosophy.
p. 105	Dionysii Longini de Sublimitate Libellus. Joannis Hudsoni.
p. 10	Aristotelis de Poetica Liber.

Front Row

p. 162	Œuvres de M.ʳ L'Abbe de Saint-Real 4 Toms.
p. 187	Histoire des Deux Triumvirats Depuis La Mort de Catilina 2 Toms. *Historie de l'Academie Francoise par M. Pelisson. *Historie de l'Academie Francoise par d'Olivet.
p. 142	Loix de Platon par le traducteur de la Republique 2 Toms. La Poetique d'Aristote Traduite en Francois par M.ʳ Dacier.
p. 10	La Rhetorique d'Aristote Traduite en Francois par M.ʳ Cassandre.
p. 155	Œuvres Du P. Rapin 3 Toms. La Logique ou l'Art de Penser.
Sheet 53 p. 48	Joannis Clerici Opera Philosophica 4 Vols. in 2.
p. 48	—— —— —— —— Ars Critica 3 Toms.

Top of front Row

	Ripley's Select Original Letters on Various Subjects ——
p. 104	Logan's Elements of the Philosophy of History. Synopsis of Lectures on Bell lettres & Logic Read in the University of S.ᵗ Andrews ——.

---

* Written on the verso of Sheet 51, and marked to be inserted here

Bonar

Second front Row

p. 141

Philosophia Vetus et Nova Ad Usum Scholæ Accommodata in Regia Burgundia Olim Portractata—— A Joh: Bapt. du Hamel 6 Toms.

Shelf 3ᵈ

Nouvelle Methode pour Apprendre Facilement La Langue Grecque.

Elementa Linguae Graecae, Studio Jacobi Moor.

Linguæ Græcæ Institutiones Grammaticæ.

Lennep in Analogiam Linguae Graecae.

p. 191

De Praecipuis Graecae Dictionis Idiotismis et Particulis Auctore Francisco Vigero.

p. 76

A Short Introduction to English Grammar by Louth.

Grammaire Generale et Raissonnee.

p. 7

Grammaire Italienne Pratique et Raissonnee par M. Antonini.

Sheet 54
p. 190

Le Maitre Italien dans sa Derniere Perfection par Veneroni.

p. 156

Principes Generaux et Raisonnes de la Grammaire Francoise par M. Restant.

L'Art de Bien Parler Francois par M. Touche 2 Toms.

p. 75

Vrais Principes de la Langue Francoise par Girard.

p. 75

Synonymes francois par Girard. Et Traite de la Prosodie Francoise par D'Olivet.

p. 1

Observations de L'Academie Francoise sur les Remarques de M. Vaugelas. 2 Toms.

p. 68

Jo. Alberti Fabricii Bibliotheca 3 Toms.

p. 68

Jo. Alberti Fabricii Bibliotheca Latina Mediæ et Infimæ Ætatis 6 Vols.

Lying on the top

p. 33

Remarques Nouvelles sur la Langue Francoise par Bouhours.

p. 81

Harwood's Lives & Characters of the Greek & Roman Classics 2 Vols.

*Harwood's View of the Various Editions of the Greek &

* Written on the verso of Sheet 53, and marked to be inserted here.

Roman Classics, With Remarks. ——

Front Row

Traite Des Sons de la Langue Francoise.
Les Elemens Primitifs des Langues par M. Bergier.
Traite de la Formation Mechanique des Langues, et des
Principes Physiques de L'Etymologie 2 Toms.
Traite des Tropes. pour Servir d'Introduction A la Rhetorique
et a la Logique par M. Marsais.

Vetus Græcia Illustrata Ubbonis Emmii Frisii.
Nic. Cragii Ripensis de Republica Lacedæmoniorum.
M. Antonii Mureti Variarum Lectionum.

Shelf 4th

Sophoclis Tragoediæ, Opera Thomæ Johnson 3 Toms.
Dionysii Halicarnassensis Opera Omnia Graece et Latine
5 Vols.
Polybii Lycortæ F. Megalopolitani Historiarum Jacobus
Gronovius 3 Vols.
Æschinis Socratici Dialogi, Vertit et Notis Illustrauit Joannes
Clericus.
Orphei Argonautica Hymni Libellus de Lapidibus et Frag-
menta Jo.. Matthias Gensnervs.
Hieroclis Philosophi Alexandrini in Aurea Carmina Com-
mentarius.
Hieroclis Philosophi Alexandrini Commentarius in Aurea
Carmina Pet: Needham.
Maximi Tyrii Dissertationes.
Hermogenis Ars Oratoria Absolvtissima, et Libri Omnes.
Aphthonius, Hermogenes, & Longinus. Greek.
L. Annæi Flori Epitome Rerum Romanarum J. G. Graevii
2 Vols.
Justinus Cum Notis Selectissimis Variorum.
Valerii Maximi Exemplorum Memorabilium Antonius Thy-
sius.

Front Row

Bonar

*Apollodori Atheniensis Grammatiici[*sic*] Bibliotheces, sive de Deorum Origine. ——

*Eunapius Sardianus. de vitis Philosophorum et Sophistarum.

p. 163   C. Crispi Sallustii Opera Omnia. Quæ Exstant.

C. Julii Cæsaris quæ extant Omnia J. G. Gævii.

Pomponius Melae. A. Gronovii.

Vegetius Renatus et alii Scriptores Antiqui de Re Militari.

Stewechii Commentarius ad Vegetium Renatum de Re Militari.

Sexti Julii Frontini quae Extant. Robertus Keuchenius.

p. 191   Sexti Aurelii Victoris Historiae Romanae Sam. Pitiscus.

p. 74   Auli Gellii Noctes Atticae. Jacobi Oiseli.

Aur. Theodosii Macrobii Opera J. Gronovii.

p. 83   Historiae Augustae Scriptores 2 Toms.

Sheet 57   Shelf 5th

Dionysii Petavii Rationarium Temporum 2 Vols.

p. 124   Ockley's History of the Saracens 2 Vols.

An Account of Denmark as it was in the Yr. 1692. An Account of Sueden [*sic*], as it was in the Year 1688.

Cours D'Etude pour L'Instruction du Prince De Parme par M. Condillac 12 Toms.

p. 188   Histoire Civile et Naturelle du Royaume De Siam Par M Turpin 2 Toms.

p. 26   Voyages De Francois Bernier. Contenant la Description des Etats du Grand Mogol &c. 2 Toms.

p. 44   Histoire et Description Generale de la Nouvelle France Par Charlevoix 6 Toms.

Lying on the top

Annales de L'Empire Depuis Charlemagne. par [*sic*].

p. 77   Relation du Voyage fait En Egypte par Le Sieur Granger, En L'annee 1730.

Front Row

Lettres Sur La Hollande 2 Toms.

* Written on the verso of Sheet 55, and marked to be inserted here.

Bonar	
Sheet 58	Front Row
p. 33	Histoire Des Guerres et des Negociations qui Precederent Le Traite de Westphalie. par Bougeant 6 Toms.
	Le Droit Public Germanique 2 Toms.
	†Histoire des Decouvertes et Conq [*sic*].
	De Rebus Publicis Hanseaticis 2 Toms.
p. 39	Augerii Gislenii Busbequii Omnia Quæ extant.
p. 99	Histoire des Decouvertes et Conquestes des Portugais Dans Le Nouveau Monde, par Francois Lafitau 4 Toms.
	Recherches Philosophiques sur les Americains, par M. de P. 3 Toms.
	Recherches Philosophiques sur les Egyptiens et Les Chinois, par M. P. 2 Toms.
	Voyage d'Un Philosophe.
Sheet 59	Shelf 6th
p. 124	Memoires of the Regency of the Late Duke of Orleans, During the Minority of Lewis the 15th.
p. 140	An Enquiry into the Cause of the Pestilence.
	Dialogues on the Uses of Foreign Travel, between Lord Shaftesbury & Mr. Locke.
	Philosophical Essays.
p. 68	Ferguson's Institutes of Moral Philosophy, for the Use of Students.
p. 105	Artis Logicæ Compendium.
p. 68	Conferences de L'Academie Royale de Peinture et de Sculpture par Mr. Felibien.
	Pensees sur L'Interpretation de la Nature.
	Lettres de Ninon de L'Enclos au Marquis de Sevigne.
p. 61	Memoires Pour Servir a L'Histoire Des Moeurs du 18. Siecle par M. Duclos.
	Considerations Sur les Moeurs de ce Siecle par M. Duclos.
p. 51	Lettres de la Marquise de M:. au Comte de R:. 2 Toms.
p. 51	Les Egaremens du Coeur et de L'Esprit, ou Memoires de Mr. Meilcour, par Crebillon.

† Struck out by a straight stroke.

Bonar	Arnoldi Vinnii Tractatus de Jurisdictione, Pactis, Transactionibus, Collationibus.
	Salmon's View of the Families of the present English Nobility.
Sheet 60	———— ———— View of the Familys of the Scottish Nobility.
p. 163	———— ———— View of the Families of the present Irish Nobility.
	Code Frederic; ou Corps de Droit, pour Les Etats de sa Majeste Le Roi de Prusse. par A. A. de C. 3 Toms.
	Ecrits Pour & Contre Les Immunities, Pretendues par Le Clerge de France. 5 Toms.
p. 69	Patriarcha: or the Natural Power of Kings, by Sir Robt Filmer Bart.
	Parecbolæ sive Excerpta e Corpore Statutorum Universitatis Oxoniensis.
	Molyneux Case of Ireland's being Bound by Acts of Parliament in England, Stated.
	Bishop of Carlile's Border Laws.
	Forbes's Methodical Treatise Concerning Bills of Exchange.
	———— ———— Institutes of the Law of Scotland 2 Vols.
p. 164	Schutzii Compendium Juris.
	Benezets Potent Enemies of America Laid Open.
	———— ———— Caution & Warning to G. Britain and Her Colonies.
p. 23	———— ———— Historical Account of Guinea.

Front Row

p. 21	Introduction Generale A l'Etude de la Politique des Finances et du Commerce. par M. Beausobre 2 Toms.

Sheet 61

Shelf 7th

Removed to the Right Hand Book Case next the door.
†Hawkin's Treatise of the Pleas of the Croun.
†Hale's History of the Pleas of the Croun. 2 Vols.
†Foster's Report of Some Proceedings on the Commission of

—————
† Struck out by straight strokes.

Bonar	Oyer and Terminer & Goal Delivery, for the Trial of the Rebels in the Year 1746 and of other Croun Cases.
	†Kaimes Principles of Equity.
p. 108	Madox's History, and Antiquities of the Exchequer of the Kings of England.
	—— —— Historical Essay Concerning the Cities, Touns [*sic*] & Buroughs of England Taken from Records.
p. 45	*Chaucers Works.
	Publii Virgilii Opera. Petri Burmanni 2 Toms.
p. 83	*Thesaurus Historiae Helveticae.
p. 111	*Joannis Marianae Historiae de rebus Hispaniae four Vols in two.
	Georgii Buchanani Scoti, Opera Omnia.
	Explicatio Tabularum Anatomicarum Bartholomaei Eusta-
Sheet 62	chii, Anatomici Summi.
p. 82	Les Loix Ecclesiastiques de France. par M. Hericourt.
	Ralph's History of England: During the Reigns of K. William, Q. Anne, and K. George I. With an Intro- ductory Review of the Reigns of the Royal Brothers, Charles and James 2 Vols.
p. 80	La Istoria D'Italia di M. Francesco Guicciardini 2 Vols.

Sheet 63	**BOOK CASE OVER THE CHIMNEY PIECE**

Upper Row

p. 82	Herodoti Halicarnassensis Historia ex Editione Jacobi Gronovii 9 Vols.
p. 56	Demosthenis Orationes Philippicae Duodecim.
p. 186	Thucydidis Bellum Peloponnesiacum 8 Vols.
	Xenophontis Graecorum Res Gestae et Agesilaus 4 Vols.
p. 191	Virgilii Maronis Bucolica Georgica et Æneis 2 Vols in one.
p. 183	La Gierusalemme Liberata di Torquato Tasso 2 Vols.
p. 115	Poesie del Signor Abate Pietro Metastasio 9 Toms.
p. 154	Le Theatre de M. Quinault. 5 Toms.

† Struck out by straight strokes.
* Written on the verso of Sheet 60, and marked to be inserted here.

Bonar

Left Hand Book Case

Shelf 1ˢᵗ

p. 56	Œuvres de Madame et de Mademoiselle Deshoulieres 2 Toms.
p. 45	Œuvres de L'Abbe de Chaulieu 2 Toms.
p. 118	Œuvres de Moliere 8 Toms.
p. 124	Œuvres de M. Nivelle de la Chaussee 5 Toms.
p. 115	Œuvres de M. Regnard 4 Toms.
p. 154	Œuvres de Racine 3 Toms.
Sheet 64 p. 51	Œuvres de M. de Crebillon 3 Toms.

Lying on the top

p. 118	*Les Philosophes, Comedie en Trois Actes, en vers par M. Montenoy.
p. 44	*Essai sur L'Union de la Poesie et de la Musique.

Shelf 2ᵈ

Melanges de Litterature, D'Histoire, et de Philosophia 5 Toms.

De L'Esprit 2 Toms.

p. 201 Œuvres Diverses de M. Rousseau de Geneve. 2 Toms.

Œuvres de M. Houdar de La Motte 11 Toms. Tom Second, contains 2ᵈ part of Tom first.

Shelf 3ᵈ

p. 140	Le Rime di Francesco Petrarca.
p. 54	La Divina Commedia di Dante Alighieri 2 Toms.
p. 26	Orlando Innamorato di Matteo M Bojardo, Rifatto da Francesco Berni 4 Toms.
p. 10	Orlando Purioso di Ludovico Ariosto 4 Toms.
p. 10	Comedie di M. Ludovico Ariosto.

en on the verso of Sheet 63, and marked to be inserted here.

Bonar	
p. 50	Il Torrachione Desolato di Bartholommeo Corsini 2 Toms.
p. 101	Il Malmantile Racquistato di Lorenzo Lippi.
p. 80	Il Pastor Fido.
	Il Primo Libro Dell' Opere Burlesche 3 Toms.
Sheet 65 p. 164	Arcadia del Dignissimo Homo Messer Jacobo Sannazaro.
	Aminta Favola Boscareccia di Torquato Tasso.
p. 80	Poesie D'Allessandro Guidi.
	Poese et Rime di Messere Giovanni Della Casa, par Antonini.
p. 43	Il Libro del Cortegiano del Conte Baldesar Castiglione.
p. 23	Raccolta di Lettere Scritte de Cardinal Bentivoglio.

Shelf 4th

p. 50	Theatre de Pierre Corneille, avec des Commentaires 12 Toms.
p. 192	Œuvres de Mr. De voltaire 9 Toms.

Right Hand Book Case

Shelf 1st

p. 160	Œuvres de Rousseau 5 Toms.
	Œuvres du Comte Antoine Hamilton 2 Toms.
p. 77	Memoires du comte de Grammont par Antoine Hamilton 4 Toms.
	Histoire Amoureuse des Gaules par le Comte de Bussi Rabutin 5 Toms.
Sheet 66	Memoire du Cardinal de Retz. 4 Toms.
	Memoires de Guy Joli Conseiller Au Chastelet de Paris 3 Toms.
p. 112	M. Valerii Martialis Epigrammatum 2 Toms.

Shelf 2d

p. 142	Œuvres de Theatre de M. Piron 2 Toms.
	Œuvres de M. de Fontenelle 8 Toms.
p. 70	Fables Choisies Mises en vers par M. de la Fontaine, avec

Bonar

p. 31

La Vie D'Esope.

Œuvres de Nicolas Boileau 4 Toms.

Les Provinciales, ou Lettres Ecrites par Louis de Montalte 3 Toms.

Theocrite quae Extant.

p. 31

Boetii Consolationis Philosophiae.

Cornelii Nepotis Excellentium Imperatorium Vitae.

Shelf 3ᵈ

p. 130   Opere del Pandre Paolo 6 Vols.

p. 106   Opere di Niccolo Macchiavelli 8 Toms.

p. 40   C. Julii Caesaris 3 Toms.

p. 183   C. Cornelii Taciti Opera quae Supersunt 4 T.

Sheet 67

Lying on the top

Caii Plinii Caecilii secundi Opera quae supersunt Omnia 2 Toms.

Shelf 4ᵗʰ

Due Tragedie: La Merope e la Demodice.

Delle Satire e Rime del Divino Ludovico Ariosto.

Julie ou La Nouvelle Heloise, par Rousseau 6 Toms.

p. 160   Emile ou de L'Education par Rousseau 4 Tom.

Dictionnaire de Chymie 2 Toms.

Dictionnaire des Arts et Metiers. 2 Toms.

Dictionnaire Raisonne Universel d'Histoire Naturelle par M. Bomare 5 Toms.

On the top

Revolution de L'Amerique par M. L'Abbe Raynal.

Sheet 68

BOOKS IN LOCKED PRESS

Shelf 1ˢᵗ

Bonar

Shuckford's Creation and fall of Man.

———— ———— Sacrad [*sic*] & Prophane [*sic*] History of the World Connected   3 Vols.

Prideaux Connection of the Old and New Testament in the Hist.ᵞ of the Jews & Neighbouring Nations   4 Vols.

Clarendon's History of the Rebellion & Civil Wars in Ireland.

p. 47 ———— ———— History of the Rebellion and Civil Wars in England, Begun in the Yᵣ 1641. 6 Vols.

p. 47 ———— ———— His Life, Written by Himself 3 Vols.

Crouch's Complete View of the British Customs 2 Vols.

p. 55 History of our National Debts and Taxes, from the Year 1688 to the Year 1751. 2 Vols.

p. 5 Almanach Royal Année 1765.

Euclidis Posteriores Libri 9.

Lawries Tables of Simple & Compound Interest.

p. 195 A Proposal for Uniformity of Weights and Measures in Scotland.

Bald's Farmer & Corn Dealers Assistant.

Harris's Philological Inquiries, in three parts.

Sheet 69   Shelf 2ᵈ

Justi Lipsi V. C. Opera Omnia   4 Toms.

p. 184 Publii Terentii Carthaginiensis Afri Comoediae. 6.

Virgilii Maronis Ouera 3 Toms.

Catullus Tibullus et Propertius, Josephi Scaligeri.

p. 96 D: Junii Juvenalis & Auli Persii Flacci Satyræ.

p. 179 Publii Papinii Statii Opera.

p. 48 Claudiani Opera Jo. Matthia Gesnero.

M Minucii Felicis Octavius.

Lucii Coelii Lactantii Firmiani Opera. quæ extant Omnia.

p. 164 Poetarum Scotorum Musae Sacræ. 2 Toms.

Jo: Barclaii Argenis. two Toms in One.

p. 17 Euphormionis Lusinini sive Jo. Barclaii Satyricon.

Sheet 70   Shelf 3ᵈ

p. 141 (?) Louthorp's Philosophical Transactions & Collections, to the

Bonar

	end of the Year 1700 Abridged & Disposed under General Heads 3 Vols.
p. 141 (?)	Jones's Philosophical Transactions from the Year 1700 to the Year 1720 Abridged & disposed under General Heads 2 Vols.
p. 141 (?)	Eames & Martyn's Philosophical Transactions, from the Year 1719, to the Year 1733 Abridged and disposed under General Heads 2 Vols.
p. 141 (?)	Philosophical Transactions, Giving some Account of the Undertakings Vols 56. 59. 60. 61. 62. 63. 64.
	Spratts History of the Royal-Society of London, for the Improving of Natural Knowledge.
p. 32	Joh. Alphonsus Borellus de Motu Animalium 2 Toms.
p. 72	Opere Del Galileo 2 Toms.
Sheet 71	Recherches sur L'Usage des Feuilles dans les Plantes, par Charles Bonnet.
p. 32	Essai Analytique sur les Facultes de Lame. par C: Bonnet.
p. 197	Exposition Anatomique de La structure du Corps Humain, par Jacques Berrigne Winslow.
p. 21	La Science des Ingenieurs dans la Conduite des Travaux de Fortification et d'Architecture Civile, dediee au Roy par M: Belidor.
p. 167	Simpson's Nature & Laws of Chance.

Shelf 4th

	Albius Tibullus.
	Propertii Elegiarum Libri Quatuor, Jani Brouk husii.
p. 184	P: Terentii Afri Comoediae Sex, Curavit Henr: Westerhovius. 2 Toms.
	Annaei Lucani Pharsalia, cum Commentario Petri Burmanni.
Sheet 72 p. 96	D. Junii Juvenalis Aquinatis Satyræ H: C: Henninius.
p. 112	M: Valerii Martialis Epigrammatum, ad usum Delphini.
p. 15	D: Magni Ausonii Burdigalensis Opera.
p. 111	Ammianus Marcellinus Jacobo Gronovii.
p 74 (?)	Auli Gellii Noctiumatticarum, Jacobus Gronovii.
	Auctores Latinae Linguæ in unum Redacti Corpus Dionysii Gothofredi.

Bonar

p. 7   Grammaticæ Latinæ Auctores Antique.
        Epitome Thesauri Antiqvitatum.
p. 145 Dictionnaire ou Traite de La Police Generale des Villes,
        Bourges, Paroisses et seigneuries de la Champagne par
        M: Freminville.
        La Droit Public de France par M. Bouquet.
p. 105 Conferences des Ordonnances de Louis 14. par M. Bornier.
        2 Toms.

Shelf 5th

p. 49   Memoires de Messire Philippe de Commines.
        Jovii Historia.
p. 185 Jacobi Augusti Thuani Historiarum 5 Toms.
p. 78   Hugonis Grotii Annales et Historia de Rebus Belgicis.
p. 151 Pufendorf de Rebus Gestis Friderici Wilhelmi Magni, Elec-
        toris Brandenburgici Commentariorum 2 Toms.
Sheet 73
p. 115 Histoire de France, Depuis Faramond Jusqua Maintenant
        par Mezeray 3 T:
p. 181 Struvii Corpus Historiæ Germanicæ 2 Toms.
p. 56   Demosthenes Opera. Greek.
p. 13   Arriani Historia Indica Jacobi Gronovii.

Shelf 6th

p. 36   Brown's Dissertation on the Rise, Union, & power; The
        progressions, Seperations[sic], & Corruptions, of Poetry
        & Music.
p. 93   Jones's Speeches of Isæus in Causes Concerning the Law of
        Succession to property at Athens.
p. 108 Macpherson's Translation of Tingal [sic], an Ancient Epic
        Poem.
p. 108 ——— ——— Translation of Tamora an Ancient Epic
        Poem.
p. 175 Smith's Gallic Antiquities.
p. 88   Howard's State of Prisons in England & Wales.
p. 146 Political Essays Concerning the present State of the British
        Empire.

Bonar

	Considerations on the Trade & Finances of this Kingdom, & on the measures of Administration.
Sheet 74	Examen de la Reponse de M. N: au Memoire par Morellet.
p. 61	Memoire pour Le Sieur Dupleix.
p. 99	Memoire Pour Le Comte de Lally.
p. 114	Recherches Sur La Population par M. Messance.
	Macpherson's Critical Dissertation, on the Origin, ——— Antiquities, Language, Government, Manners & Religion of the Ancient Caledonians.
p. 108	An Introduction to the History of Great Britain & Ireland by James Macpherson.
p. 15	Bacon's Works 4 Vols.
	Euclidis Elementorum Libri 15.
	Trigonometria Britannica.
	Arithmetica Logarithmica.
	Kersey's Elements of that Mathematical Art Commonly Called Algebra.
p. 77	Astoromicæ Physicæ & Geometricæ Elementa Auctore Davide Gregorio.
p. 78	Grew's Anatomy of Plants; with an Idea of a Philosophical History of Plants.
p. 86	Hook's Physiological Descriptions of Minute Bodies, mode [*sic*] by Magnifying Glasses.
p. 111	Marcelli Malpighii Philosophi et Medici Bononiensis Opera Omnia 3 Toms.

Sheet 75   Shelf 7th

p. 168 (?)	Skene's Old Laws and Constitution of Scotland.
	Coke's Institutes of the Laws of England, or a Commentary upon Littleton, in four parts 3 Vols.
p. 34	Brady's Complete History of England, from the first Entrance of the Romans under Julius Caesar, to the End of the Reign of King Henry 3.
p. 34	——— ——— Continuation of the Complete History of England: Containing the Lives & Reigns of Edward the 1. 2. & 3. & Richard the Second.
p. 34	——— ——— Introduction to the Old English History.

Bonar	
(cf. p. 34)	—— —— Historical Treatise of Cities & Boroughs.
p. 189	Tyrrell's General History of England Ecclesiastical & Civil 5 Vols.
p. 39	Burnets History of the Reformation of the Church of England 3 V^s.
p. 39	—— —— Memoires of the Lives & Actions of James & William Dukes of Hamilton &^{c}. In Seven Books.
p. 196	Whitlock's Memorials of the English Affairs; Containing the publick Transactions Civil & Military.
Sheet 76	Spelman's Works.
p. 31	Boethii Historiæ Scotorum.
p. 50	Cowley's Works.

Lying on the top

p. 13	Arnot's History of Edinburgh.
p. 89	Hume of Godscrofts History of the House of Douglas and Angus.

Sheet 77	**Left Hand Window Book Case**
p. 18	Oluvres [*sic*] Diverses de M^r. Pierre Bayle 4 Toms.
p. 68	Basilii Fabri Thesaurus Eruditionis Scholasticæ 2 Toms.
	†A Variety of Maps. Scots Atlas.
	Atlas D'Anville.
	American Atlas.
	Homans Atlas.
	Fricx's Maps.
	Blair's Chronology and History of the World, From the Creation to the Year of Christ 1768.
	A Complete List of the Commissioners, Collectors, Compt^{rs} &^{c} &^{c} &^{c} in his Majesty's Revenue of the Customs.
p. 6	Anderson's Diplomatum Scotiæ.
p. 82	Bibliotheque Orientale, ou Dictionnaire Universel. par M: D: Herbelot.
p. 196	Whitworth's State of the Trade of G: Britain, in its Imports & Exports progressively from the Year 1697.
(cf. p. 121)	Postlethwayt's History of the publick Revenue.

† Struck out by a straight stroke (the first four words).

Bonar

Sheet 78   **Right Hand Window Book Case**

p. 83   Hobbes's Leviathan, or the Matter, Forme & Power of a Commonwealth Ecclesiastical and Civill.

        Puffendorf Droit de La Nature 2 Toms.

p. 190   Le Droit des Gens ou Principes de la Loi Naturelle par M. Vattel. ———

p. 92   Hutcheson's System of Moral Philosophy 2 Vols.

p. 118   Œuvres de Monsieur de Montesquieu 3 Toms.

p. 27   Institutions Politiques. par M. Le Baron de Bielfeld 2 T^s.

        Ferguson's Essay on the History of Civil Society.

p. 115   Millar's Observations Concerning the Distinction of Ranks in Society.

p. 172   Smith's Inquiry into the Nature and Causes of the Wealth of Nations 2 Vols.

        Another Copy 2 Vols.

p. 180   Steuarts Inquiry into the principles of Political Economy: Being an Essay on the Science of domestic Policy in free Nations 2 Vols.

p. 40   Campbell's Political Survey of Britain: being a Series of Reflections on the Situation, Lands Inhabitants &c &c of this Island 2 Vols.

Sheet 79   Shelf 2^d

Hawkins Treatise of the Pleas of the Crown.

Sir Matthew Hale's History of the Pleas of the Crown. 2 Vols.

Foster's report of some proceedings on the Commission of Oyer & Terminer & Goal delivery, for the Trial of the Rebels in the Year 1746 in the County of Surrey, & of other Crown Cases. ———

p. 66 (?)   Kaime's Principles of Equity.

        Hutcheson's Calculations & Remarks relating to the present state of the public debt and Funds.

        Anno Regni Georgii 3 Regis Vicesimo Primo. 2 Toms.

p. 72   Dictionnaire Universel Contenant Generalement tous les Mots

Bonar

Francois, Tant vieux que Modernes, et les Termes des
Sciences et des Arts par M. Furetiere 4 Toms.

p. 76

Glossarium ad Scriptores Medeæ & Infimæ Latinitatis par du
Fresne 2 Toms.

Sheet 80

Lying on the top

Marci Antonini Imperatoris T: Gataheri. 2 Toms.

Sheet 81

BOOKS IN CLOSET

Right Hand Book Case

Shelf 1ˢᵗ

p. 156   Present State of the Republick of Letters 7 Vols.

p. 172   Smith Von Nation Reichthumern.

p. 78   Hugonis Grotii Annales et Historiae de Rebus Belgicis.

Origin and Progress of Languages Vol 1.

Mair's Book-keeping.

Smillies Translation of Buffon's Natural History, General
and Particular 8 Vols.

Carver's Travels Through the Interior Parts of North America in the Year's 1766, 1767, and 1768.

p. 119   Moores View of Society and Manners in France, Switzerland,
Germany & Italy. 4 Vols.

Macfaits New System of General Geography. Two
Coppies [*sic*].

Sheet 82

Shelf 2ᵈ

The London and Gentlemans Magazine from the Year 1769
to the Year 1777 both Inclusive 18 Vols.

p. 167   Roberto Simson Sectionum Conicarum Libri 5.

On the top

Macfaits New System of General Geography Two Copies.

Bonar

Shelf 3ᵈ

The Parliamentary Register; or History of the proceedings
and Debates of the House of Lords and Commons, from
the Year 1774 to the Year 1781 Inclusive 18 Vols.

Sheet 83

Shelf 4ᵗʰ

Prior Documents, or a Collection of Interesting Authentic
Papers, Relative to the Dispute between Great Britain &
America; Shewing the Causes & Progress of that Mis-
understanding from the Year 1764 to 1775.

p. 5 Journal of the proceedings of Congress Held at Philadelphia,
from Septᵗ. 5ᵗʰ 1775 to April 30ᵗʰ 1776.

The Remembrancer, or Impartial Repository of Public
Events, from the Year 1776 to 1780 Inclusive 10 Vols.

p. 107 Mackay's Abridgement of the Excise-Laws.

p. 168 Smith's Theory of Moral Sentiments, with a dissertation on
the Origin of Languages.

Sheet 84

Shelf 5ᵗʰ

p. 124 Nugents Grand Touer [*sic*] through the Netherlands, Germany, Italy and France 4 Vols.

p. 49 Journal of a Tour to Italy by M: de la Condamine.

Memoires ou Observations Sur L'Italie par deux Gentils-
hommes Suedois 3 Toms.

p. 141 Nouveau Voyage de France par M. Piganiol [*sic*] de la Force
2 Toms.

p. 141 Abbrege Chronologique de L'Histoire et du Droit Public
D'Allemagne, par M. Pfeffel 2 Toms.

p. 65 Epicteti Stoici Philosophi Enchiridion.

Excerpta Quedam ex Luciani Samosatensis Operibus par N:
Kent.

p. 33 Recherches sur L'origine du Despotisme Oriental.

L'Antiquite de Voilee par ses Usages par M. Boulanger
3 Toms.

<table>
</table>

Bonar

	Traite des Delits et des Peines.
	Hum's [*sic*] Four dissertations.
p. 90	—— Philosophical Essays.
p. 52	De Ligibus [*sic*] Naturæ disquisitio Philosophica. Authore Ricardo Cumberland.
(*cf.* p. 98)	Kaim's Essays on the Principles of Morality & Natural Religion.

Sheet 85   Shelf 6th

p. 113	Memoire Pour Le Comte de Lally.
	Antunt Metaphysics: Or the Science of Universals.
p. 53	Dalrymples Annals of Scotland, from the Accession of Robert I surnamed Bruce, to the Accession of the house of Stewart.
	Stuarts View of Society in Europe, in its progress from Rudeness to Refinement.
p. 5	The History of North America, from the Year 1497 to 1763.
p. 151	Priestly's Course of Lectures on Oratory and Criticism.
	Russian Code of Laws.
p. 163	Salmon's London Art of Building.
	Life and Acts of Robert Bruce King of Scotland.
	—— —— of William Wallace of Ellerslee.
	Vitriarii Prælectiones in Grot: de Jure.
p. 37	Summa Bullarii, sev Constitutionum.
	Historiarum de Regno Italiæ.
p. 71	Francisci Assisiatis Opuscula.
p. 58	The Precipitation and fall of Messrs Douglas, Heron, & Company, late Bankers in Air, with the Causes of their distress & Ruin.
	Pursuers Memorial in the Douglas Cause.
	Information for Wm Leechman Principal of the College of Glasgow & other Professors Pursuers; Again Dr Robt Trail land others. Professors in the College of Glasgow defenders.
	Proof in the Conjoined proces [*sic*] of Hamilton Against Douglas.
p. 181	Stuarts Letters to Lord Mansfield.

Bonar

Memoire et Consultation, sur une Question du droit des Gens. ———

Sheet 86   Shelf 7th

p. 37   De Asse et Partibus ejus Libri quinqe Guellulmi Budei Parisiensis Secritarii Regii.

p. 124   Onuphrii Panvinii Veronesis Fratris Eremitæ Augustiniani Rupublicæ Romanæ Commentariorum Libri Tres.

p. 166   Caroli Sigonii De Antiqvo ivre Civium Romanorum Italiæ Provinciarum Ac Romanæ Jurisprudentia Ivdiciis, Libri 11th.

p. 31   Bodini Andegavensis de Republica.
          Quintilia Institutionem Oratoria.

p. 165   L: Annaeus Seneca A. M. Antonio Mureto Correctus et Notis Illustratus ———

p. 37   Omnia Opera Gulielmi Budaei.

p. 142   Platonis Opera.

p. 163   Cl: Salmasii Plinianae Exercitationes in Caii Julii Solini Polyhistora. 2 Toms.

p. 165   Sexti Empirici Opera quæ Extant.

p. 142   Platonis Omnia Opera Vitvstissimorum Exemplarium.

p. 57   Dionis Cassii Cocceiani Historiæ.

p. 111   Marcelli Malpighii Opera Omnia.
          Burrow on the Customs.

Sheet 87   **Ground, or Under Shelf of Left Hand Closet Book Case**

Anno Regni Georgii 3d Regis Vicesimo 2 Vols.
Anno Regni Georgii 3d Regis Decimo Nono 2 Vols.
Anno Regnii [*sic*] Georgii 3d Regis Decimo Octavo 2 Vols.

PLATES

Adam Smith's Library at the Tokyo University.

The bookplate of Adam Smith. (4×6 cm)

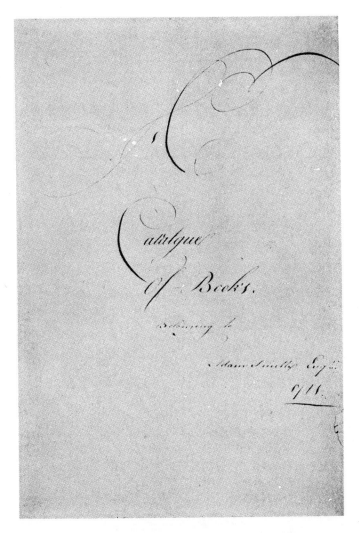

First page of the Catalogue of Adam Smith's Library, 1781.
(reduced from folio size)

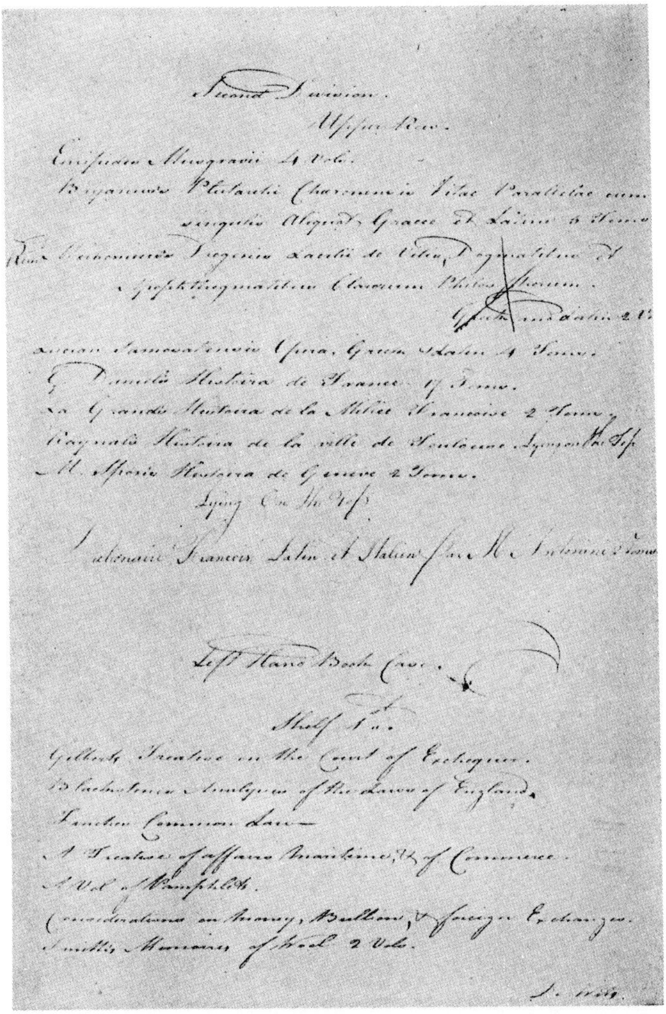

Second Division.

Upper Row.

Ejusdem Musgravii 4 Vols.
Bryanus Plutarchi Chaeronensis Vitae Parallelae cum singulis aliquot, Graece et Latine 5 Tomi
[illegible] Diogenis Laertii de Vitis, Dogmatibus et Apophthegmatibus Clarorum Philosophorum.
[illegible] 2 V.
[illegible] Opera, Graece Latine 4 Tom.
G. Daniels Histoire de France 17 Tom.
La Grande Histoire de la Milice Francoise 2 Tom.
Raynals Histoire de la ville de Toulouse [illegible]
M. Spons Histoire de Geneve 2 Tom.

Lying On the Top.

Dictionaire François Latin et Italien par M. Antonini 2 Tom.

Left Hand Book Case.

Shelf 1st.

Gilberts Treatise on the Court of Exchequer.
Blackstones Analysis of the Laws of England.
Finches Common Law
A Treatise of affairs Maritime, & of Commerce.
A Vol. of Pamphlets.
Considerations on Money, Bullion, & foreign Exchanges.
Smiths Memoirs of Wool 2 Vols.

[illegible]

P. 10 of the Catalogue of Adam Smith's Library, 1781.

Untersuchung

der Natur und Ursachen

von

Nationalreichthümern

von

Adam Smith,

Beyder Rechte Doktor, Mitglied der königlichen Gesellschaft der
Wissenschaften zu London und ehemaligem Lehrer der Moral-
philosophie auf der Universität zu Glasgow.

Aus dem Englischen.

Erster Band.

Leipzig,
bey Weidmanns Erben und Reich. 1776.

The title-page of the German Translation of
"The Wealth of Nations," Vol. I, 1776.

The engraved added title-page of Thomas Hobbes' Leviathan.

THE ADAM SMITH LIBRARY

Works by Adam Smith

AN INQUIRY INTO THE NATURE AND CAUSES OF THE WEALTH OF NATIONS

[1776]

2 volumes, medium quarto

The first facsimile of the original edition of the most famous book in economics. In two bindings: *de luxe*, bound in full antiqued calf, stamped in gold, with a slip case; library, bound in sturdiest buckram.

THE THEORY OF MORAL SENTIMENTS

[1759]

Adam Smith's first major work; indispensable for an understanding of the basic philosophy underlying *The Wealth of Nations*. A reprint of the latest Bohn Library issue of 1892. x, 506 pp.

LECTURES ON JUSTICE, POLICE, REVENUE AND ARMS

[1763]

Edited with an introduction and notes by EDWIN CANNAN

[1898]

Student notes of Adam Smith's course at the University of Glasgow; his early work on economics. xli, 293 pp.

THE EARLY WRITINGS OF ADAM SMITH

Edited with an introduction by J. RALPH LINDGREN

This volume includes: Preface to William Hamilton's *Poems*, writings in *The Edinburgh Review* of 1755, *Essays on Philosophical Subjects*, *Considerations Concerning the First Formation of Languages*.

The first complete collection of Adam Smith's early writings. 255 pp.

Books on The Life of Adam Smith

THE LIFE OF ADAM SMITH
[1895]
By JOHN RAE
With an Introduction
"Guide to John Rae's *Life of Adam Smith*" by Jacob Viner

A handsome reprint of the most important *Life*, with an introduction which appraises the present state of knowledge about the life of Adam Smith, written by the leading contemporary authority. 146, xv, 449 pp.

ADAM SMITH, AS STUDENT AND PROFESSOR
[1937]
By WILLIAM R. SCOTT

Second in importance ony to John Rae's *Life*, this book, illustrated with pictures and facsimiles of documents, preserves a wide variety of source material concerning Adam Smith's life and work chiefly at the University of Glasgow. Crown octavo, xxv, 445 pp.

BIOGRAPHICAL MEMOIRS OF ADAM SMITH
By DUGALD STEWART

Written in 1793, Dugald Stewart's *Memoir* is the first biography of Adam Smith, and the only one by a contemporary, friend and fellow student of economics and philosophy. Reprinted from Volume X of Stewart's *Collected Works*, with about 30 pages of notes added in 1811 and further material added in 1858. The complete volume which includes *Memoirs* of William Robertson, Thomas Reid and Dugald Stewart himself is reprinted. clxxvii, 338 pp.

Adam Smith's Own Library

A CATALOGUE OF THE LIBRARY OF ADAM SMITH
By JAMES BONAR
2nd edition, 1932   xxiv, 218 pp.

A FULL AND DETAILED CATALOGUE OF BOOKS
WHICH BELONGED TO ADAM SMITH
[1951]
By YADAO YANAIHARA
ix, 126 pp. and plates

These two volumes list most of the books known to have belonged to Adam Smith. A most detailed account of Adam Smith's library appears in Jacob Viner's introduction to John Rae's *Life of Adam Smith*.

Contemporary Discussions of The Wealth of Nations

A LETTER FROM GOVERNOR POWNALL TO ADAM SMITH
[1776]

By THOMAS POWNALL

This comment on *The Wealth of Nations*, published in the same year, is one of the first and is particularly interesting since it was written by a governor of the colony of Massachusetts. 48 pp., 8½ x 11.

THE STATE OF THE POOR

Or, A History of the Labouring Classes in England, from the Conquest to the present period . . .
[1797]

By SIR FREDERIC MORTON EDEN

3 vols.   Crown quarto

This great collection of information about the working classes of England in the 18th century forms a valuable background to the ideas of Adam Smith.

AN INQUIRY INTO THE NATURE AND ORIGIN OF PUBLIC WEALTH—AND INTO THE MEANS OF ITS INCREASE
[1804]

By JAMES MAITLAND, 8th Earl of Lauderdale

An early major critique of *The Wealth of Nations*. 500 pp.

OBSERVATONS ON THE SUBJECTS TREATED IN DR. SMITH'S INQUIRY . . . 2nd EDITION
[1817]

By DAVID BUCHANAN

A volume of essays added to Buchanan's edition of *The Wealth of Nations* which was the first annotated edition. Comments from what became the Malthusian point of view. xvi, 316, 88 pp.

A TREATISE ON POLITICAL ECONOMY
[1821]

By JEAN-BAPTISTE SAY

Say's work, written in 1803, translated into English in 1821, is credited with putting Adam Smith's views in a more logical form. It is in this form that Smith's views were widely propagated throughout the nineteenth century and even in our day. lx, 488 pp.

NEW PRINCIPLES ON THE SUBJECT OF POLITICAL ECONOMY
[1834]

By JOHN RAE

A major critique of *The Wealth of Nations,* based on experience of life in the United States and Canada; attacks free trade, emphasizes sociological factors in capital formation; pioneer study of economc development. xvi, 414 pp.

Modern Comment on Adam Smith's Work

MONETARY THEORY BEFORE ADAM SMITH
[1923]

By ARTHUR E. MONROE

The outstanding modern treatise on monetary theory before Adam Smith, with special emphasis on the eighteenth century. xi, 312 pp.

THE SPIRIT OF '76 AND OTHER ESSAYS
[1927]

By CARL BECKER, J. M. CLARK, WILLIAM E. DODD

Lectures in commemoration of the 150th anniversary of *The Wealth of Nations* and *The Declaration of Independence.* 135 pp.

ADAM SMITH 1776-1926
[1928]

By J. M. CLARK, PAUL H. DOUGLAS, JACOB H. HOLLANDER, GLENN R. MORROW, MELCHIOR PALYI, and JACOB VINER

Comments on various aspects of Adam Smith's work and significance 150 years after the publication of *The Wealth of Nations.* ix, 241 pp.

PREDECESSORS OF ADAM SMITH
[1937]

By E. A. J. JOHNSON

The growth of British economic thought before Adam Smith, with an exposition of the ideas of the leading British mercantilist writers, xiii, 423 pp.

For additional information about *The Adam Smith Library,* its privileges and conditions of membership, please write the publisher:

AUGUSTUS M. KELLEY · *Publishers*
24 East 22nd Street, New York, New York 10010